WITHDRAWN FROM STOCK
The University of Liverpool

THE ABSORPTION
OF SOLUTES
BY
PLANT CELLS

THE ABSORPTION
OF SOLUTES
BY
PLANT CELLS

D. H. JENNINGS

The Botany Department
Leeds University

OLIVER & BOYD

EDINBURGH AND LONDON

OLIVER AND BOYD LTD

Tweeddale Court
Edinburgh 1

39a Welbeck Street
London, W.1

First published 1963

Printed in Great Britain
by T. and A. CONSTABLE LTD., Hopetoun Street
Printers to the University of Edinburgh

PREFACE

The reasons for the appearance of this book should be apparent in the introductory chapter. I do not want to add anything further here except the hope that the book will both encourage further experimental work and also provide a useful introduction for those who are not directly concerned but who wish to know more about the subject.

It is a pleasure to acknowledge the help of a number of people throughout the writing and the production of this book. I should like to thank Professors I. Manton F.R.S. and R. D. Preston F.R.S. for their encouragement and help and Miss J. M. Denison for her valuable assistance with the typing. Mr. D. Ainslie Thin has assisted the book through the production stage and has ironed out a number of grammatical irregularities in the final manuscript, for which I am very grateful. My thanks are due to those who kindly and willingly gave their permission for the inclusion of various tables and figures in the text. My especial thanks are due to Drs. J. L. Harley and A. Rothstein for many stimulating and valuable discussions about many of the topics included in the book. The development of my interest in this field of plant physiology owes immeasurably to the happy association with each of them in experimental studies on solute absorption by plant cells.

ACKNOWLEDGEMENTS

I am grateful to the following for permission to reproduce text figures and tables:—

Academic Press Inc., New York, for Fig. 5a, from *Archives of Biochemistry and Biophysics*, **63**, 93, 1956 (Fig. 2).

Acta Physiologica Scandinavica for Table 4.

American Society of Plant Physiologists for Figs. 11, 12, 13, 14, 15 and Table 7.

The Biochemical Journal for Fig. 19 and Table 5.

The Clarendon Press, Oxford, for Fig. 4.

The Commonwealth Scientific and Industrial Research Organization for Fig. 16, from *Australian Journal of Biological Sciences*, **12**, 415, 1959 (Fig. 2).

Gebrüder Borntraeger, Berlin, for Table 2, from *Protoplasma*, **6**, 611, 1921 (Table 1).

The Journal of General Physiology for Figs. 3, 10, 17 and Tables 3, 8.

Long Island Biological Association for Fig. 2, from *Cold Spring Harbor Symposium*, **8**, 206, 1940 (Fig. 1).

The Macmillan Co. Inc., New York for Table 6.

Nature for Figs. 20, 21.

Pergamon Press Ltd., Oxford, for Figs. 7a and b, from the article by G. E. Briggs, A. B. Hope and M. G. Pitman in *Radioisotopes in Scientific Research*, editor R. C. Extermann, **4**, 391-400, 1958 (Figs. 3b and 4b).

The Royal Society for Fig. 18.

Society for Experimental Biology for Table 1.

Springer-Verlag, Berlin, for Fig. 9, from *Handbuch der experimentellen Pharmakologie*, **13**, 59, 1960 (Fig. 2a).

University Press Cambridge for Fig. 1, from H. Davson and J. F. Danielli: *The Permeability of Natural Membranes* (Fig. 73).

The Wistar Institution of Anatomy and Biology for Figs. 6a, from Fig. 4, A Rothstein and M. Bruce, *J. Cell. Comp. Physiol.* **51**, 153, 1958, and 6b from Fig. 6, A. Rothstein and M. Bruce, *J. Cell. Comp. Physiol.* **15**, 155, 1958.

CONTENTS

Chapter 1

INTRODUCTION

The experimental facts concerning the movements of solutes between plant cells and the external medium are discussed in this book. It has been written in the belief that it is revealing to compare the facts obtained with bacteria, fungi, algae and higher plants relating to the movements of substances between the cell and the external medium. The subject-matter has been divided as follows: the first five chapters are of a general nature, while the later chapters are devoted to the absorption of specific ions or molecules by plant cells. This structure emphasises the need to consider separately the absorption of each ion or molecule. There is no reason to believe that an absorption mechanism for a specific solute need necessarily differ from one plant cell to another; however, within any one plant cell the same mechanism need not be responsible for the absorption of all ions of like sign or for molecules of similar chemical composition.

Plant cells show a capacity to accumulate a variety of solutes. In some cases, accumulation may be the result of binding to cellular constituents. In other cases, accumulation of a solute may be brought about through a difference between the ionic equilibrium of a compound encountered in the cell and that encountered in the external medium, when only one component of the equilibrium, frequently the undissociated molecule, is able to penetrate into the cell. Again, accumulation might be explained by chemical alteration, a situation which must be anticipated in all cases where the solute is a substance of metabolic importance. In a large number of cases it is not possible to explain the accumulation of solute within the cell by such means. The solute moves into the cell against an activity gradient, the movement being linked in a specific manner to metabolic events within the cell. At this stage it is not appropriate to discuss in detail the concept of active transport, which is used to describe the accumulation of ions or molecules within a cell in this manner. While the concept of active transport is unambiguous for non-electrolytes, the active transport of electrolytes is complicated by ionic charge. In considering the accumulation of any ion within a cell, the movements of other ions must also be considered. The movement of an ion will be accompanied by the production of an electrical potential which will influence the movement of other ions. Thus, accumulation of a certain cation will be balanced either by the movement of an equivalent number of different cations in the opposite direction or an equivalent number of anions in the same direction. It is clear that the movement of an ion against an activity gradient may be brought about by the active transport of another ion. Rigid criteria must then be established before any conclusions are drawn concerning the actual ions which are actively transported. A complete picture of the accompanying ion movements and changes in electrochemical potential is necessary before it can be decided that any one ion is being moved into the cell by active transport.

The ability of plant cells to concentrate solutes is well established, but this should not overshadow the fact that cells are able to maintain their internal environment independently of changes in the external medium. Frequently, plant cells are extremely permeable to many solutes, yet the same cells readily discriminate between the various molecules or ions in solution. The two problems—accumulation of solutes by plant cells and the maintenance of the internal environment of the same cells—are interrelated, and in certain cases the same mechanism must be involved, as for example when a solute is maintained at a higher concentration than in the external medium. On the other hand, the mechanisms maintaining the internal environment of the cell may be excretory in nature or purely passive in the form of barriers to diffusion.

A number of parameters must be investigated before the relationship between the plant cell and solutes in the external medium can be defined. The large number of factors which can influence solute movement between plant cells and the external environment provide the rationale for this book and the emphasis on the demonstration of the wide variety and multiplicity of ionic and molecular interchange between cells and the external solution.

CHAPTER 2

THEORETICAL CONSIDERATIONS

Introduction

The mechanisms by which solutes pass into the interior of cells have not been classified in detail, but the distinction into active and passive transport has considerable value. On occasion, there has been a certain ambiguity in the use of the term active transport. Active transport means that the cell is performing work in moving the solute into the cell. Metabolic processes are closely involved often in a stoichiometric manner, though the exact manner in which these processes exert their influence upon the specific transport of a solute is not clear in the great majority of cases. A number of hypotheses have been advanced to explain the linkage between metabolism and the transport mechanism, but until recently the experimentalist has been virtually unable to indicate in an individual case what type of mechanism might be operating. This last difficulty may well have led to those ambiguities which have occurred.

The actual mechanism, through which metabolism brings about the transport of a solute into the cell, could equally be either a chemical or a mechanical event such as the folding of a membrane (provided of course that such an event showed a marked specificity towards the solute in question). It must be emphasised that, whatever the nature of the mechanism of active transport, metabolism acts through a discrete event. Thus the transport of a solute in consequence of gross metabolic activity, such as the maintenance of a concentration gradient between the outside of the cell and the inside or the maintenance of an electrochemical potential across the cell membrane, cannot be considered as active transport. The limited conclusions which can be drawn from experiments in which the rate of metabolism is reduced are a practical consequence of this restriction of gross metabolic phenomena from a definition of active transport. It cannot be concluded that active transport mechanisms are involved if the rate of entry of various solutes is reduced as the result of reducing the rate of metabolism (for instance by the use of inhibitors or by the use of anaerobic conditions). Unspecific processes are equally likely to be implicated in governing the rate of solute entry.

This critique of experimental evidence may be carried further. It has been frequently suggested, in view of the metabolic nature of active transport, that the demonstration of active transport can be considered fairly conclusive if the system shows, at most, the following characteristics:

1. The temperature coefficient is high, of the same order as enzymic reactions.

2. The rate of absorption is not a linear function of the difference in concentration between the external medium and the interior of the cell. Similarity between the kinetics of absorption to enzyme kinetics is taken as even stronger evidence.

3. Competition for entry between similar substances in a manner similar to competitive inhibition of enzyme activity.

4. The rate of absorption is very different for substances, although structurally related, having similar molecular size and lipoid solubility.

5. Inhibition of absorption is possible with a variety of enzyme poisons.

This outlook has been determined to a great extent by the key role played by Michaelis-Menton kinetics in enzyme studies. It is obvious that, in the kinetic analysis of any data arising from the study of a biological phenomenon, the data should be first analysed in terms of Michaelis-Menton kinetics. In certain cases, such an analysis can be valuable, not only in defining the system involved but also for the comparison of related systems. It will be seen that such an analysis is possible for certain problems associated with the cellular absorptions of solutes. If Michaelis-Menton kinetics are to be applied to problems of solute transport, confusion can arise at two points. First, it is imperative that the kinetic treatment be rigorous. Qualitative agreement can be misleading simply for the reason that other models are possible which show such characteristics as limitation in rate at higher concentrations and competition between similar molecular configurations. Furthermore, if the absorption of the solute is the result of metabolic activity without being brought about by a specific transport process, the rate of absorption will inevitably be describable in terms of Michaelis-Menton kinetics—a reflection of the dependence of the process on general metabolic reactions.

The criteria which have been postulated above can be criticised on more general grounds. It has been customary to accept that, in all those cases where the rate of absorption shows a dependence on temperature, the penetration of the solute must necessarily be under the control of metabolism. Rosenberg (1954) has pointed out that the biologist is often interested primarily in the existence of control mechanisms and is less interested in whether changes in the rate of absorption are brought by changes in the resistance of the cell or changes in the driving forces. This outlook in some ways must be responsible for the conclusion that, where a system shows properties which are similar to those of an enzyme, the system must be connected in direct manner with the metabolism of the cell.

This general criticism bespeaks something of the lack of awareness shown by those studying transport problems of the factors which govern the rate of passive penetration of a solute into a cell. It will be seen that the absorption of a solute, which is temperature dependent and which shows saturation characteristics, possesses properties which are in no way incompatible with the solute entering the cell by passive means. Furthermore it will be shown that, although active transport is of major importance with respect to the absorption of physiologically important solutes, a more devious approach which considers passive mechanisms may lead to a more satisfactory elucidation of the presence of an active mechanism than that of direct attack. For, by exclusion of passive mechanisms, it is possible to infer the presence of an active mechanism. This approach has had marked success in the study of ion movements between large algal cells and the external medium. Apart from this, the experimentalist dealing with absorption of solutes by plant cells should have a clear knowledge of the various ways in which passive transport can manifest itself. Studies with animal cells have demonstrated already a variety of passive transport phenomena. The discussion which follows will lean heavily on the known instances of such passive transport phenomena and will be less concerned with a rigorous theoretical treatment. On the other hand, principles will be to the forefront rather than detailed experimental facts.

One final point which must be made before starting this discussion concerns the term 'membrane'. This term will be used rather freely, but it should not be thought that this necessarily implies a very special structural entity. In constructing model systems, discrete membranes are simpler both from practical as well as theoretical considerations. As far as biological membranes are concerned, it should be remembered constantly that there are two categories—the morphological membrane observed by the microscopist and the physiological membrane which is an *ad hoc* structure for explaining certain observations on solute absorption by cells. Physiological membranes ought to be considered as discontinuities or barriers and these may be without any gross structural and hence visible characteristics. The two categories possess properties which are probably common to both—the observed membranes providing the type of barrier predicted by physiological experiment. Studies of cell permeability, particularly those which have demonstrated a correlation between the rate of penetration of non-electrolytes and their oil-water partition coefficients, suggest that the permeability barriers consist largely of lipoid substances. Those membranes which have been observed with the aid of the electron microscope bounding cells and within the cytoplasm almost certainly consist in part of oriented lipoids, which make them strong candidates for the necessary barriers to penetration of, at least, non-electrolytes. Although membranes are widely distributed throughout the cytoplasm, from the logical point of view, in so far as it is the membrane in contact with the external solution, the outer membrane of the cytoplasm or plasmalemma would be the major permeability barrier. Entry into the interior of the cytoplasm might also be made through those invaginations of the plasmalemma which ramify and join with other membrane systems within the cytoplasm itself.

Water and a number of solutes, especially electrolytes, penetrate living cells at rates very much greater than can be expected if they had to traverse a lipoid membrane. This would mean that the membrane must not be homogeneous and must contain some aqueous channels through which these molecules may pass. It is probable that the membrane through its structure and composition possesses other means whereby molecules with low lipoid solubility may penetrate more rapidly. This need not mean that the various active transport mechanisms necessarily reside in the membrane. However, experimental evidence is indeed in favour of the active transport mechanism, which is responsible for the transport of potassium into and the transport of sodium out of nerve cells and erythrocytes, residing in the observed outer membrane of these cells. Nevertheless, further evidence will be presented which shows that active mechanisms are not only associated with the outer region of the cell but also with the tonoplast. There is also evidence from studies with yeast that the cell may contain a number of permeability barriers to the solute in question (in this case hydrogen ions). Whether such barriers reside in the numerous membranes which can be seen within the cytoplasm of plant cells with the aid of the electron microscope remains to be seen.

One reason for the location of the major permeability barrier in the plasmalemma lies in it being the first possible barrier that a solute must penetrate when entering the cell. Deductions about this location depend greatly on the plasmalemma being both a stable structure and a continuous barrier. It now seems that neither property is strictly applicable. It has been known for some time that the plasma membrane of animal cells is capable of engulfing fluid from the external medium, and the discrete droplets so formed are carried into the interior of the cell. This phenomenon is known as *pinocytosis* and was first observed by W. H. Lewis in 1931. With the advent of more refined light microscopical methods and the identification of pinocytosis vacuoles by electron microscopy, interest has been revived in this phenomenon (Holter, 1959; Rustad, 1961). The most important finding has been that this process shows specificity—the number of pinocytosis vacuoles depending on the constitution of the external medium. Pinocytosis has not been observed directly in plant cells, in fact attempted observation of pinocytosis in yeast protoplasts has failed (Holter and Ottolenghi, 1960). However, Jensen and McLaren (1960) have suggested that pinocytosis is responsible for the observed distribution of radioactivity in barley and onion root tips after varying periods in solutions of ^{14}C and ^{3}H labelled haemo-globin, lyzozyme or ribonuclease. Bhide and Brachet (1960) have also suggested that pinocytosis must be operating to account for the distribution of absorbed ribonuclease, as measured by enzyme activity, in onion roots. These conclusions may be questioned, but there is no doubt that the plasmalemma of plant cells is capable of dramatic changes of physical shape, changes which far exceed anything normally associated with stretching (Manton, 1961). While the phenomenon of pino-cytosis can very seriously undermine the structural edifices erected on the basis of models postulated from kinetic formula-tions, such observations of membrane movements provide another feature which, apart from the possible direct effect on solute movement, must be accounted for when relating the structure of the membrane to its permeability properties.

Passive transport

The simplest case of passive transport is free diffusion, namely the movement of a solute in which the rate of movement is determined by a difference in concentration and is propor-tional to that difference in concentration. The situation is described by Fick's equation

$$\frac{ds}{dt} = -D \cdot \frac{dc}{dx},$$

where ds is the amount of substance diffusing across an area 1 cm.[2], in time dt, for a concentration gradient of $\frac{dc}{dx}$, and D is a constant. This equation is applicable only when the resistance to diffusion is continuous—that is in a medium where the particle size is small compared with that of the diffusing molecule. If diffusion is across a solvent layer which is very large compared with that of the diameter of the diffusing molecule, Fick's equation is found to hold. With biological systems, Fick's equation is only roughly true. In such systems, there will certainly be discontinuous resistance to a diffusing molecule, especially so if the path of movement is through a membrane whose thickness is of the order of 10 μ.

If the boundary concerned is a phase of unknown thickness such as a membrane, it is usual to use a permeability coefficient P (instead of D) and assume nothing about the concentration gradient.

Therefore $$\frac{ds}{dt} = P(C_1 - C_2).$$

The movement or *flux* across the boundary is then given by

$$\phi = P(C_1 - C_2),$$

i.e. the amount moving per unit area per unit time is given by the product of the permeability coefficient and the difference in concentration across the boundary. The dimensions of D are cm.^{2} sec.$^{-1}$ and those of P are cm. sec.$^{-1}$, provided that the concentration is in moles per cm.^{3}. The flux is then expressed in moles per cm.^{2} sec. It should be noted that the permeability coefficient is a property of both the boundary and the solute and for this reason is much more applicable to biological systems than Fick's constant D.

Fick's constant is a measure of the resistance offered to free diffusion. In water the values of D are thousands of times less than in a gas at normal temperature and pressure due to resistance offered by the Van der Waals' and other forces acting between the molecules. The simplest relation between D and the molecular size is given by the relationship due to Thovert who applied Maxwell's equation to diffusion in liquids;

$$DM^{\frac{1}{3}} = \text{a constant},$$

where M is the molecular weight of the solute in question. This expression is very roughly true for molecules up to the size of hexoses diffusing in such solvents as water and alcohol.

The effect of temperature on a system obeying Fick's law can be predicted, if it is assumed that the system is acting as a perfect gas. A rise in temperature will increase the kinetic energy of the molecules in the solution. In a perfect gas, the kinetic energy per molecule is given by

$$\tfrac{1}{2}nm\bar{u}^2,$$

where n is the number of molecules in a given volume, m is the

B

mass of the molecule and $\bar{u}$ is the root mean square velocity. The relationship between the velocity of the molecules and temperature is given by

$$\tfrac{1}{3}Nm\bar{u}^2 = RT,$$

where $N = $ Avogadro's number.

The effect of a ten-degree rise in temperature will be given by

$$\frac{\bar{u}_{T+10}}{\bar{u}_T} = \sqrt{\frac{T+10}{T}}\,.$$

The ratio $\dfrac{\bar{u}_{T+10}}{\bar{u}_T}$ is known as the temperature coefficient and is symbolised by Q_{10}. In the range 20° to 30°, the Q_{10} should have a value of 1·02. In actual fact, the Q_{10} of diffusion in water in this range lies between 1·2 for rapidly diffusing molecules and 1·5 for very slow molecules. The deviations from the value found for perfect gases are due to molecular interactions which are occurring in the liquid. With liquids of higher viscosity, the molecular restraints are much greater with consequent higher values of Q_{10}. From the practical standpoint, when dealing with the absorption of a solute by plant cells, a low Q_{10} could indicate diffusion, but, as will be apparent in the succeeding comments, it provides little information about the interaction of the solute molecules with the membranes of the cell. However, if the system is characterised by a low Q_{10} and obeys the relationship $DM^{\frac{1}{2}} = $ a constant, it is likely that one is dealing with diffusion in water or some other liquid of comparatively low viscosity. This might be the case in membranes which are described as 'leaky'.

It is clear from the Q_{10} values quoted that diffusion in a liquid shows marked deviation from what will be expected from a perfect gas. Indeed, as Danielli (1943) has pointed out, diffusion in liquids and also of course solids must be considered as a discontinuous process in which at one moment a molecule may be moving rapidly from one point to another in the medium and at another moment the molecule is merely vibrating and rotating about a mean position in the medium. The molecule is restrained in this position by the forces between the molecule and those neighbouring. The molecule may be regarded as being surrounded by a potential energy barrier and it can only pass over this barrier when it receives sufficient kinetic energy. It will then be free to diffuse until it loses its kinetic energy. The temperature coefficient of diffusion is determined by the height of the potential energy barriers.

Danielli (1943) has considered possible potential energy barriers which might confront a solute molecule penetrating a cell. He has pointed out that, if the restriction to penetration resides in the outer membrane of the cell, there will be three sites where there will be resistance: first, the membrane interface for diffusion in the direction water→membrane; second, the membrane interior; and third, the inner membrane interface. Previous to the considerations put forward by Danielli, only the second site had been considered, but, with membranes of the dimensions and composition of those in living cells, this neglect of the other two sites is not justifiable. The potential energy relationships of the three sites of resistance may be represented diagrammatically (Fig. 1).

Danielli has shown that a relationship can be derived for this situation provided that certain assumptions are made. It is assumed that the height of the potential energy maxima and minima does not vary with time and that the diffusing molecules diffuse only when they possess the minimum kinetic energy which is necessary to break the bonds restricting diffusion. The analysis can be started by considering the diffusion through a section 1 cm.^{2} of a membrane which contains n maxima. If the concentration at one side is C_0 and at the other C_n, with concentrations at successive minima C_1, C_2, C_3, . . . , C_n, under conditions of steady flow, ~~the rate of~~ which across the membrane will be $\dfrac{ds}{dt}$, the rate of passage of solute molecules from C_0 to C_1 will be

$$\frac{dN_0}{dt} = eC_0 \, ,$$

where e is a constant and is a function of μ_e. Similarly, the rate of flow from C_1 to C_0 will be given by

$$\frac{dN_1}{dt} = eC_1 \, .$$

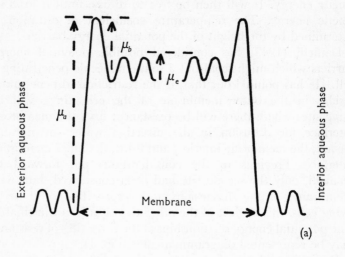

(a)

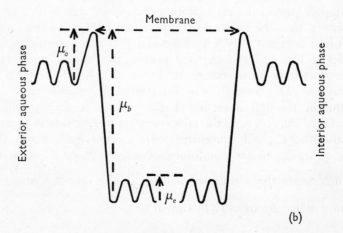

(b)

Fig. 1. Potential energy diagrams of the cell membrane: the potential energy barriers met (a) by a molecule such as glycerol, (b) by a molecule such as benzene or propane (Danielli, 1943).

Hence the net rate of flow from C_0 to C_1 is

$$\frac{dN_0}{dt} - \frac{dN_1}{dt} = \frac{ds}{dt} = e(C_0 - C_1)\ .$$

Therefore

$$\frac{ds}{dt} = \frac{e}{n}(C_0 - C_n).$$

It is now possible to consider the flow across the interfaces between the membrane and the media on each side. The concentrations on the two sides are kept steady at C and C_i respectively. Under conditions of steady flow,

$$\frac{ds}{dt} = aC - bC_0 = bC_n - aC_i$$

$$= \frac{a}{2}(C - C_i) - \frac{b}{2}(C_0 - C_n).$$

Therefore, from above,

$$C_0 - C_n = \frac{a}{b + 2e/n} \cdot (C - C_i)\ ;$$

substituting from above,

$$\frac{ds}{dt} = \frac{e}{n} \cdot \frac{a}{b + 2e/n} \cdot (C - C_i).$$

But since

$$\frac{ds}{dt} = P(C - C_i)\ ,$$

where $P =$ the permeability constant,

$$P = \frac{ae}{nb + 2e}\ .$$

This then defines the permeability of a homogeneous membrane. In applying the relationship to a specific case, it is necessary to evaluate the terms, a, b, e and n. The relative values of a and b can be obtained from the partition coefficient B, where

$$B = \frac{a}{b}\ .$$

Danielli has given a semi-empirical equation to evaluate e and has suggested that the thickness of the membrane will be a maximum measure of n. Using these evaluations, it is possible to derive expressions for the following situations—for molecules which encounter the main resistance to penetration in the interior of the membrane

$$PM^2 = \text{a constant} \; ;$$

on the other hand, for molecules which encounter the main resistance to penetration at the interface of the membrane

$$PM^{\frac{1}{2}}e^{2500x/RT/B} = \text{a constant} \, ,$$

where x is the number of unscreened —CH_2 groups in the molecule, providing a measure of the activation energy of diffusion of non-polar groups into water which involves an energy of 2500 calories per group. For both the situations just mentioned,

$$PM^{\frac{1}{2}}Q_{10}^{(T+10)/10} = \text{a constant} \, .$$

Table 1 gives some examples showing the extent to which these relationships are obeyed by permeability measurements obtained with living cells. For the data obtained with the diatom *Melosira* and the green alga *Chara ceratophylla*, P is taken as the partition coefficient for olive oil-water.

TABLE 1

Values of $PM^{\frac{1}{2}}/B \times 10^{13}$ for *Melosira*

(Danielli, 1952)

Propionamide	7·2	Glycerol	4·5
Acetamide	2·0	Methylurea	2·3
Glycol	6·1	Urea	2·2

Values of $PM^{\frac{1}{2}}e^{2500x/RT} \times 10^4/B$ for *Chara ceratophylla*

(Danielli, 1952)

Erythitol	8·5	Urotropin	6·3
Methylolurea	10·9	Methylurea	8·3
Urea	5·8	Dicyandiamide	9·4
Glycerol	6·5	Lactamide	6·4
Malonamide	5·5		

There are a number of points which arise from this simple theory of *activated* diffusion as proposed by Danielli. First, it was concluded from such results as those given above that most cells, both plant and animal, have to a first approximation a membrane which is fundamentally lipoid and which is homogeneous in nature. The rate of penetration of some types of molecule, notably ionic species, is too fast to be accounted for by simple diffusion through a lipoid membrane. In such cases, it was proposed that the molecules penetrate through certain small areas of the membrane which possess special properties. Second, this theory is important to the general discussion of transport phenomena in that it demonstrates the unsuitability of Q_{10} as a criterion for the presence of an active mechanism. A high Q_{10} of penetration is completely compatible with the operation of a passive mechanism.

In spite of the complexities which arise when considering diffusion through thin membranes, in all cases up to this point the dependence of the rate of diffusion upon the concentration of the diffusing solute is simple—the rate of diffusion is linearly related to the difference in concentration on the two sides of the membrane. Studies with mammalian erythrocytes have shown that the penetration of a number of molecules, which although being passive in nature, does not obey this simple relationship between rate of penetration and concentration difference. Furthermore, the rate of penetration was found to be very much greater than would be expected if the molecules were penetrating a homogeneous lipoid membrane by activated diffusion. Both glycerol and glucose penetrate erythrocytes in this manner, and our knowledge of this mechanism of passive transport rests on the data obtained with these two molecular species (see Bowyer, 1957; LeFevre, 1954 and 1961; Willbrandt, 1954, for reviews of such work).

The characteristics of the penetration of these two substances into erythrocytes can be enumerated:

1. Transport leads to equalisation of concentration between the cell and the external medium. Up to now, accumulation has not been demonstrated.

2. As has been pointed out, the rate of penetration is many times greater than can be expected if the molecule were passing through a homogeneous lipoid membrane.

3. With increasing concentration in the external medium, the rate of penetration does not increase proportionally.

4. Structurally related compounds are frequently unable to penetrate at the same rate. The cell membrane may indeed be impermeable to these compounds. *Meso*-inositol is unable to penetrate into erythrocytes. This compound is an isomer of glucose with a ring structure and steric arrangement of hydroxyl groups similar to glucose, with the exception that it is homo-cyclic and has no reducing group. This suggests that the mechanism has some degree of specificity.

5. Penetration of one compound is frequently inhibited by the presence of structurally related compounds in the external solution. Thus mannose reduces the penetration of glucose, and glycerol penetration is reduced by the glycol 1 : 2-dihydroxypropane and vice versa. This evidence confirms the suggestion in para. 4 above that the mechanism is specific for a small range of structurally related compounds and that competition for entry takes place between such compounds.

6. While no inhibition is observed with metabolic poisons such as sodium azide or dinitrophenol, certain specific poisons can bring about cessation of penetration. Penetration of glucose is inhibited by dinitrofluorobenzine, p-chloromercuribenzoate and phlorizin; the penetration of glycerol is inhibited by cupric ions.

There is no doubt that neither glucose nor glycerol nor related compounds penetrate human erythrocytes by simple diffusion. On the other hand, the inability of the system to accumulate either of these compounds and the insensitivity of penetration to metabolic poisons indicates that active mechanisms are not concerned. *Facilitated diffusion* has been proposed (Danielli, 1954) as a name for the mechanism possessing those characteristics just enumerated.

A major feature of the molecules which penetrate by facilitated diffusion is their polar nature, in consequence of which they readily form hydrogen bonds with water. All the mechanisms which have been proposed to account for facilitated diffusion are based on the severence of the hydrogen bonds between water and the compound which is diffusing and the formation of hydrogen bonds between the compound and some molecule within the membrane itself. The postulated mechanisms can be classified into the following three groups.

1. The diffusing molecule combines with a carrier and is transported across the membrane by a carrier. A model of this system can be represented (LeFevre, 1954):

$$\begin{array}{c|c|c} \text{Outside} & \text{Cell membrane} & \text{Inside} \\ & k_1 \qquad k_3 & \\ B+ & A\rightleftharpoons A - B\rightleftharpoons A & +B \\ & k_2 \qquad k_4 & \end{array}$$

This type of model has been suggested by a number of authors with varying degrees of modification.

2. Diffusion takes place through a channel in the membrane whose walls have a hydrogen bonding structure (Stein and Danielli, 1956). The presence of protein lamellae which extend through the membrane could provide the necessary structure, for, when two protein lamellae are face to face, the space between them is a hydrogen bonding space which will have a highly specific configuration and which will account for the selective nature of the process of facilitated diffusion.

Both types of mechanism postulated are susceptible to similar kinetic analysis. Thus Stein and Danielli derive the following basic relationship for the movement of glycerol into erythrocytes. They assume that the inward flux (i.e. the movement of molecules in *only* the inward direction across the membrane) obeys a limiting law of the Michaelis type.

Thus
$$\text{Flux}_{\text{inwards}} = \frac{\phi_{\max} C}{K + C},$$

where $\phi_{\max}$ = the maximum rate of flux and C = the concentration of solute in the external medium.

Similarly
$$\text{Flux}_{\text{outwards}} = \frac{\phi_{\max} C_i}{K + C_i},$$

where C_i = the concentration of the solute inside the cell. The net flux will be the net movement of molecules across the membrane, and the rate of net flux $\frac{ds}{dt}$ will be given by Fick's law

$$P(\text{flux}_{\text{inwards}} - \text{flux}_{\text{outwards}}).$$

Thus $$\frac{ds}{dt} = \phi_{max}P\left(\frac{C}{K+C} - \frac{C_i}{K+C_i}\right).$$

This type of relationship is capable of more sophisticated analysis, but for the purpose of this discussion it is enough to say that many of the experimental facts fit this type of relationship.

3. The above models are based on the fact that the membrane offers alternative hydrogen bonding to that of water molecules. However, Stein (1961a and b) has proposed an alternative method by which a penetrating solute can have its hydrogen bonds saturated in such a manner that it can traverse the membrane. Stein suggested that two solute molecules interact together to form a dimer and this reduces the number of hydrogen bonds. The dimers, free of attached water molecules, are able to enter the hydrophobic regions of the membrane. Inside the membrane, the dimers dissociate from the site of dimerisation and can then traverse the membrane (either as dimers or for the most part, having dissociated, as monomers). Stein postulated as part of the mechanism the existence, as a constituent of the cell membrane but exterior to the lipoid component, of a novel type of enzyme—a 'dimeriser'.* Such an enzyme has in common with other enzymes the property of binding its substrate to form the classic Michaelis-Menton complex. But a dimeriser differs from most other enzymes in a number of ways. Firstly, the bond between the substrate and enzyme is non-covalent. Secondly, rather than binding single substrates, it binds pairs of these—it is divalent towards its substrate. Thirdly, the enzyme does not bring about any covalent modification in the substrate; instead it enables the pair of molecules which are bound to it to interact with one another by hydrogen bonds to form dimers.

Stein (1961a and b) has presented evidence for this type of mechanism with data from studies of the penetration of glycerol and glucose into human erythrocytes. The strongest evidence in favour of the theory is the fact that it provides a simple explanation of the observed rates of penetration from mixtures of two solutes (A and B), in which the total concentra-

---

* 'Dimerase' was originally proposed, but the name 'dimeriser' removes the suggestion of covalent bond-formation as with a 'true' enzyme.

tion $(A + B)$ is kept constant but the relative amounts $(A : B)$ are varied.

If the relative amounts of A and B are altered, there will always be a particular ratio of A to B at which the amount of A attached to the dimeriser will be exactly equal to the amount of B similarly bound. This ratio of A to B is given by the ratio of the Michaelis constants K_A and K_B. When A and B are present in this ratio, the ratio of dimers formed will be $\frac{1}{4}AA$, $\frac{1}{4}BB$ and $\frac{1}{2}AB$. Now it may be that, by virtue of the structural features of the molecules A and B, the dimer AB is not a true dimer and cannot penetrate the membrane. It follows that there will be a minimum rate of transfer of total solute $(A + B)$ which is less than the rate of transfer of A and B when present alone. Equally, it is possible that the dimer AB is more readily formed than AA or BB and penetrates more rapidly than the latter two dimers. If this occurs, there will be a maximum rate of transfer of total solute which is greater than the rate of transfer of A and B when present alone.

Glucose-fructose mixtures show such a minimum rate of entry, while sorbose-fructose mixtures show a maximum rate of entry. With choice of suitable Michaelis constants, it is possible to predict with a good fit the behaviour of a mixture.

Whatever the actual mechanism which is responsible for facilitated diffusion, these studies with erythrocytes are a salutary reminder that the criteria such as high Q_{10} of penetration, specificity and competition between similar molecules for the transport system are of no value in identifying active mechanisms. Although facilitated diffusion occurs under the driving force of thermal agitation, the process has many characteristics of active transport owing to the fact that the diffusion of the molecules is strongly influenced by structural and steric factors. There is evidence that facilitated diffusion can occur in plant cells (see Chapter 13).

So far, the discussion has been concerned with non-electrolytes. Fundamentally, the diffusion of ions follows laws similar to those for non-electrolytes. The passive transport of either molecules or ions across a membrane can be expressed by

$$\text{flux} = \text{'permeability'} \times \text{'driving force'}.$$

If molecules are diffusing, the driving force is the difference in concentration across the membrane; whereas when ions are diffusing, the driving force is the difference in electrochemical activity across the membrane. Dainty (1960) has pointed out that this formulation is analogous to Ohm's law with flux, permeability and driving force equivalent to current, conductance and potential difference.

The force acting on an ion causing it to diffuse can be divided into two components, electrical force and the osmotic force due to the activity difference. The electrical force will be the work done in moving the ion over the distance in which diffusion is occurring. If one considers a small distance dx and the potential over that distance dE, then the work done in moving a gram ion through dx will be $zF\,dE$, where F is the Faraday constant and z the charge of the ion. The electrical force in the case of a cation will then be

$$-zF \cdot \frac{dE}{dx}.$$

The force due to the activity gradient will be

$$-RT \cdot \frac{d \ln a}{dx}.$$

A formulation for the 'permeability' of the system can be derived by considering the velocity at which the ions will be moving. The velocity of the ions can be measured in terms of the electrical conductivity. If this is so, the current will be directly proportional to the number of ions, to the charge carried per ion and to the mobility of the ions present. If the velocity (or mobility) of the ion over unit potential gradient is u, then the velocity over the gradient $\dfrac{dE}{dx}$ will be $u\dfrac{dE}{dx}$. The resistance to movement of the ions (r) will be given by the force acting $\left(F\dfrac{dE}{dx}\right)$ on the ion divided by the velocity of the ion, thus $r = \dfrac{F}{u}$. The 'permeability' of the system to the ion will be the reciprocal of this namely $\dfrac{u}{F}$. The flux (ϕ) then will be

$$\frac{u}{F}\left(-zF \cdot \frac{dE}{dx} - RT \cdot \frac{d \ln a}{dx}\right),$$

in which case

$$\phi = -zu \cdot \frac{dE}{dx} - \frac{uRT}{F} \cdot \frac{d \ln a}{dx},$$

the signs being such that the positive flux of a cation occurs when the activity and potential gradients are both negative. The flux for an anion is

$$\phi = zu \cdot \frac{dE}{dx} - \frac{uRT}{F} \cdot \frac{d \ln a}{dx}.$$

If these equations are to be solved for the transfer of an ion across a membrane, assumptions have to be made about the mobility of the ion in the membrane phase and also about the electrical potential across the membrane. Assumptions have been made with respect to these two unknown quantities, but the relationship which has been derived provides only qualitative agreement with observations made on biological systems. It is evident that the precise prediction of the penetration of ions into a cell requires more detailed information about the composition of those cytoplasmic structures through which ions must diffuse.

Despite the lack of knowledge concerning such structures, it is possible to determine whether or not the movement of an ion is brought about by passive means without the ion combining with other moving particles. This possibility exists because relationships can be derived for the passive movement of ions which are independent of those variables which are a function of cellular structure.

The electrochemical potential is a function of the gradient of chemical activity and of electrical activity and is defined by the equation

$$\bar{\mu} = \mu + RT \ln a + zFE.$$

Since the zero of electrical potential is arbitrary, the electrochemical potential is referred to that of a 'standard' state μ.

The permeability of a membrane to an ion will greatly depend upon the other ions in the system. If, for instance, the following system is considered

$$\text{outside} \quad \begin{array}{c|c} A_o^+ & A_i^+ \\ B_o' & B_i' \end{array} \quad \text{inside}$$
$$\text{Membrane}$$

then the permeability of the membrane to the cation A^+ will be determined as much by the permeability of the membrane to the anion B' as by the ability of A^+ itself to move across the membrane. If the membrane is selectively permeable to ions of one sign, a diffusion potential will be set up and this in turn will assist the movement of ions in one direction and oppose the movement of ions in the other. Thus it can be seen that whereas, when ions are diffusing in a homogeneous system where no potential is produced, the equilibrium is governed by the gradient of chemical activity, on the other hand, when a potential difference is established, the equilibrium is governed by the electrochemical potential. Therefore with a membrane system at equilibrium,

$$\bar{\mu}_o = \bar{\mu}_i .$$

This can also be written

$$RT \ln a_i + zFE_i = RT \ln a_o + zFE_o$$

$$\frac{RT}{zF} \ln \frac{a_o}{a_i} = E_i - E_0 = \Delta E ,$$

where ΔE is the electrical potential difference across the membrane. This is the Nernst equation.

The value of this relationship is twofold. If it is known that an ion moves passively without the mediation of a carrier across a membrane, it is then possible to calculate the electrical potential difference across the membrane from measurements of the cellular and the extracellular concentrations of the ion concerned under equilibrium conditions. The reverse is possible, but, under these circumstances when the electric potential can be measured, it is more useful to use the measurements of both electrical potential difference and ion concentrations. It is possible to compare the cellular ion content as it is measured with a value calculated on the basis of the measured potential difference. Agreement between the two values means that the equilibrium between the external medium and the internal environment must have been brought about by passive means. Lack of such agreement must mean that the ion concerned is being transported into or excluded from the cell by an active process.

The situation which has just been discussed can be considered from another point of view. If this system is not in equilibrium, there will be a net flux of ions in one direction, with the result that the system will move towards equilibrium. Whatever the forces (active or passive) which are bringing about the movement of the ions, the net flux for a single ion will be

$$\phi = \phi_{in} - \phi_{out},$$

ϕ_{in} being the influx of the ion and ϕ_{out} being the efflux. If the ion is moving under only the influence of an activity difference,

$$\phi_{in} = P_{in}a_o$$

where P_{in} refers to the permeability of the cell to the influx of the ion. The electrochemical potential with respect to the ion can be rewritten

$$RT \ln [a_o e^{zFE/RT}].$$

If the electrical potential is included in the consideration of the influx of the ion,

$$\phi_{in} = P_{in}a_o e^{zFE/RT},$$

and similarly

$$\phi_{out} = P_{out}a_i \, e^{zF(E-\triangle E)/RT}.$$

Thus

$$\frac{\phi_{in}}{\phi_{out}} = \frac{P_{in}}{P_{out}} \cdot \frac{a_o}{a_i} e^{zF\triangle E/RT}.$$

This relationship was first derived by Ussing (1949) and Teorell (1949) using a much more rigorous treatment. Of the two, the treatment by Ussing is preferable, since it does not require specific assumptions about the movement of the ion in the membrane itself. If the permeability of the membrane is assumed to be the same in both directions, this relationship provides a means of examining the passive nature of ion movements under conditions in which equilibrium has not been achieved, especially since radioactive tracers are so eminently suitable for measuring the individual fluxes. The actual practical procedure usually consists of labelling the ions on one side of the membrane with a suitable isotope (preferably one of reasonable half-life) and measuring its initial rate of appearance on the other side. Prolonged immersion in a medium containing the isotope is required for internal labelling, in order to ensure complete equilibration of the isotope between external and internal environments. With equilibration under such conditions, when the cell is transferred to an unlabelled medium and the efflux of the isotope determined, the specific activity of the isotope inside the cell will be known. The net flux can be determined by chemical means, and, with the measurement of one flux, the other flux can be determined by difference. This may be the only suitable method for determining the efflux.

If the observed flux ratio agrees with the calculated value, it can be reasonably assumed that the ion is moving passively across the membrane. On the other hand, lack of agreement does not preclude passive mechanisms. Discussion of actual instances is best left until the section in Chapter 6 on potassium and sodium movements in animal cells, where exchange diffusion and single-file movement of ions (passive phenomena which do not obey Ussing's equation) are described in detail. There will be no agreement between the observed and calculated flux ratio if the ion is being actively transported either into or out of the cell, but, since lack of agreement occurs when such passive mechanisms are operative, the lack of agreement provides only inconclusive evidence for the presence of an active mechanism.

Active transport

The mediation of an active mechanism in the movement of a non-polar solute into plant cells can be demonstrated in reasonably direct manner. Accumulation of the solute against a concentration gradient and the necessity of metabolism for such an accumulation are the most important criteria which must be fulfilled. On the other hand, the experimental demonstration that an active mechanism is directly responsible for the movement of an ion into a cell has many of the characteristics of a search after a will o' the wisp. The reasons that this should be so have already been given. Certain passive movements can of course be eliminated, but, if the electrical potential between the cytoplasm and the external medium cannot be determined, the problem is even more complex. Two possible approaches are left under such circumstances, namely the study of fluxes under conditions in which metabolism is extremely low or inoperative and the isolation of the carrier responsible for the active fluxes of the ion. In the first instance, by using low temperatures, anoxia or metabolic inhibitors, the active fluxes can be reduced to a low level so that passive fluxes will be operative. While it cannot be over-stressed that extreme caution is needed in extrapolating the results to the normal metabolic state, this approach must of necessity be tried. The elucidation of certain passive sodium and potassium fluxes (those which do not obey Ussing's equation) in animal cells by such an approach justifies the recommendation of this experimental procedure with plant cells.

Isolation of the carrier would be a very questionable approach, if the precedent had not already been established for animal cells. The isolation of an enzyme having all the properties required for the potassium-sodium carrier in nerve cells and erythrocytes has confirmed the earlier findings that potassium ions are absorbed by and sodium ions are excluded from these cells by an active process. The problem of isolating the carrier responsible for the active transport of a solute will be discussed later. However, all such studies depend *a priori* on the necessity for a carrier molecule for the active transport of a solute. Little speculative thought is required to formulate other means whereby a solute may be transported into the cell by an active mechanism. Mention has already been made of the possibility that membrane movements may be involved. The means whereby it should be possible to study such an active mechanism *in vitro* are too speculative to be discussed at this stage.

C

CHAPTER 3

THE PLANT CELL AS A MULTI-COMPONENT SYSTEM IN RELATION TO DISSOLVED SUBSTANCES

Visually, plant cells are extremely heterogeneous systems whose cytoplasm contains a wide variety of structures. Visual observation has shown clearly that many substances do not partition equally between cytoplasm and vacuole. It has often been easy to see that various coloured compounds are found exclusively in the vacuoles of plant cells, and observations such as these have undoubtedly given foundation to the importance of the tonoplast in maintaining the composition of the vacuole different from the cytoplasm. There has been a tendency to assume that, since vacuoles often contain such complex molecules as pigments, tannins and gums, these cellular entities are concerned with what might be loosely termed 'excretion' from the cytoplasm. Such views may be true, but they are based on too few strictly quantitative estimates. Visual observations can obviously only give a rough guide to the partition of substances between vacuolar sap and cytoplasm, especially in the majority of cells, where the cytoplasmic volume (observations often being made still more difficult by the close juxtaposition of cytoplasm and cell wall) is difficult to determine. Furthermore, conclusions drawn from observations on the distribution of large molecules may not be applicable to smaller molecules. With smaller molecules, methods of approach other than the purely visual are necessary to study the distribution of such compounds. Consideration of metabolites both inorganic and organic is in any case more significant to our understanding of such structures as vacuoles. The concept of the vacuole as an excretory reservoir has had its basis in the lack of knowledge of the metabolism of large organic molecules which are found to be associated with the vacuolar sap. Any facts concerning the movements of inorganic ions or organic compounds involved in intermediary metabolism are free from a taint which has become attached, often through ignorance, to larger molecules.

Consequently, a study of the distribution of small molecules between the cytoplasm and vacuole and within the cytoplasm becomes one invoking problems of permeability rather than one involving hypotheses of function propounded on insufficient facts; although it is clear that, as facts accumulate from such a study, it will be possible to draw firm conclusions concerning the function of cellular structures such as the vacuole.

Most of our knowledge concerning the physiology of the vacuole is derived from studies on large algal cells. The cells usually studied are those of the species of *Valonia* and *Halicystis* or the long internodal cells of *Nitella* and *Chara*. With these cells, it is easy to extract and analyse the vacuolar sap and to make electrical studies using inserted microelectrodes.

The first observations showed that the vacuolar sap of these algae invariably differs from that of the external medium in both total salt content and in ionic composition. With *Valonia*, for instance, although the total salt content of the vacuolar sap is not greatly in excess of that of an equal volume of sea water, the relative proportions of the cations, particularly sodium and potassium, are quite different. The sodium concentration in the vacuole is lower than that in sea water and the potassium content is very much higher. On the other hand, all the ions present in pond water (which of course represent a more dilute solution), with the notable exception of nitrate, are accumulated within the vacuoles of cells of *Nitella* (Table 2) (Hoagland and Davis, 1929; Collander, 1942). While the composition of the vacuolar sap of these large cells may seem relatively stable, it is still subject to a range of response to the environment (Hoagland and Davis, 1929; Steward and Martin, 1937; Collander, 1942).

It became clear that the vacuole is separated from the external medium by a barrier possessing selective properties with respect to the various ions. It was hoped that electrical methods might elucidate further the nature of this barrier. Blinks (1940) has provided a synopsis of the rationale for the early studies. It was assumed that the mobility of any pair of ion species in the protoplasmic surface (presumably across the cytoplasm—electrodes are placed in the vacuole and surrounding medium and joined by a salt bridge) is shown by changes of potential difference across the protoplasmic surface

TABLE 2

The composition of cell sap of *Nitella* collected from pond water (Hoagland and Davis, 1929)

Date of Collection†	Composition of sap or external solution (m.equiv. per l.)*								
	Cl	SO₄	H₂PO₄	Sum anions	Ca	Mg	Na	K	Sum cations
August 22 to September 12	105·5	11·9	2·0	119·4	11·7	12·1	56·2	50·8	130·8
September 23 to September 26	101·1	13·0	1·7	115·8	13·0	10·8	49·9	49·3	123·0
November 5 to November 21	102·9	17·9	2·8	123·6	11·5	16·4	40·0	59·1	127·0
Pond water, average composition (samples of August 9 and September 26)‡	1·0	0·67	0·0008	—	1·3	3·0	1·2	0·51	—

* The conductivity of the sap was approximately 25 times that of pond water. The pH of the sap was uniformly close to 5·2, whilst that of pond water varied from 7·0 to 9·0.

† First date, time of collecting cells from the pond; second date, time when the cells were taken from the tank (containing tap water of very similar composition to pond water) in the laboratory.

‡ HCO₃ also present in pond water in relatively large concentrations; NO₃ also present in pond water but not in the sap.

when the external solution is diluted, concentrated or another solution substituted for it. If the potential difference (P.D.) quickly attains a maximum and holds it in a good plateau, the salt in question is not rapidly entering or leaving the cell. On the other hand, if a solution change produces an initial large effect which then falls away, the original gradient is being impaired by entrance or exit of the salt or ion in question.

Electrical resistance is another facet of the relationship between vacuole and the cytoplasm which can be measured. This measurement was originally made in large cells with direct current, to avoid the effects of their large capacity on alternating current impedance. Resistance to current flow, while showing that there is an effective barrier to ions in the cell, does not discriminate between ions of a mixture nor does it state whether ions of only one charge or of both are being impeded in passage. However, by making solution substitutions, where only one ion is changed, it has been possible to observe large changes of resistance, which taken with the corresponding changes of potential give a good indication as to which ion is concerned. A further complication lies in the fact that measurement is made across the entire cytoplasm, so that the effect at the two surfaces (outer and vacuolar) may not be separable.

Blinks (1932) found that soon after the insertion into *Halicystis* of a fine capillary, giving direct communication to a calomel electrode, a potential difference appears across the protoplasmic surface, and within half an hour or so rises to a characteristic value (-70 mV in *H. osterhoutii* and -80 mV in *H. ovalis*). This potential can be maintained for long periods, up to several days. By examining changes in potential, Blinks was able to show that the vacuolar surface of the cytoplasm possesses different properties from those of the outer surface. Perfusion experiments, in which the contents of the vacuole are changed for sea water or an artificial medium, showed that the inner or vacuolar surface is indifferent to substitution of sodium ions for potassium (Blinks, 1935). On the other hand, the outer surface of *Halicystis* is far from indifferent to potassium. The cells respond to an increased concentration of potassium chloride in the sea water by a large change of P.D. in the positive direction (Blinks, 1932) (Fig. 2).

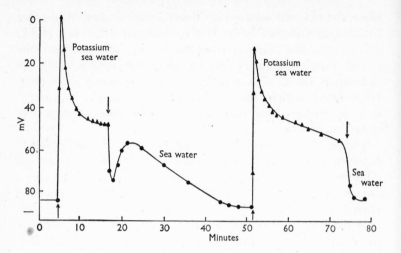

Fig. 2. The potential difference across the protoplasm of *Halicystis* in sea water and when artificial sea water containing potassium instead of sodium is externally applied. The arrows indicate the time of solution changes (Blinks, 1940).

However, the P.D. due to the increased potassium concentration in the outside medium dies away quickly, the speed of which suggests why perfusion, which is a slow operation, might not show a potassium effect at the vacuolar surface. On the other hand, it makes it likely that potassium gradients cannot be wholly responsible for the steady P.D. of *Halicystis*.

By changing the content of the external medium and measuring concomitant changes in the P.D., Blinks showed that anions such as nitrate, formate, acetate, proprionate, butyrate, lactate, pyruvate, succinate, etc. have a much lower mobility in the cytoplasm than chloride. These ions, when substituted for chloride in sea water, reduce and reverse the P.D. to a positive value. The measured P.D. in such circumstances is about +20 mV, a change of some 100 mV. On the other hand, if nitrate (or formate) sea water is substituted for sap in the vacuole by perfusion, the P.D. across the cytoplasm falls to −100 mV. Thus the effect of low mobility is about 20 to 30 mV at the vacuolar surface compared to 100 mV or more at the outer surface. Blinks (1940) suggested that in the cyto-

plasm there are similar poorly mobile organic anions of sufficient total base binding capacity to make up about 0·6 M salt
(sodium, potassium, etc.). Assuming that the anions of the cytoplasm are able to set up similar potentials against sea water
and sap at the two surfaces, there is then a potential of some
100 mV negative at the outer surface and 20 mV positive at the
inner surface. These will be minimal values, since the concentration of cytoplasmic anions may be very much higher than
0·6 M, which is the concentration applied externally. Such a
concentration could be assumed to keep the protoplasm clear of
chloride ions by simple Donnan forces, though Blinks believed
that an active mechanism is involved constantly aiding the
depletion of chloride from the cytoplasm.

Blinks also showed that, although change in the gradient of
sodium chloride between the sap and vacuole makes no difference to the P.D., dilution of sea water (with isotonic glycerol)
results in a fall in P.D., indicating that there is a gradient of
sodium chloride between the external medium and the cytoplasm. The P.D. change indicated that the sodium ion has a
lower mobility in the cytoplasm than either the chloride ion or
the potassium ion (relative mobilities being Na^+ : $0\cdot2 - 0\cdot4$,
Cl' : $1\cdot0$, K^+ : 20). Blinks suggested that the discrimination
between sodium and potassium occurs at the outer surface.

These conclusions are not entirely satisfactory. The potential
differences were measured without any concurrent estimations
of the ionic composition of the cytoplasm and the vacuolar sap.
Furthermore, the changes in P.D. are interpreted in terms of
presumed ion movements. There is no reason to suppose that
ion movements other than those postulated are not occurring.
The change in P.D. observed with dilution of external sea
water could be accounted for by movement of sodium out of the
cytoplasm. From the point of view of chemical analysis, such
movements are difficult to determine. However, radioactive
isotopes can frequently provide almost unequivocal evidence of
ion movements.

Early experiments with isotopes and large algal cells suffer
from the disadvantage that low specific activities forced workers
to use high extracellular concentrations of ions (Brooks, 1940;
Hoagland and Broyer, 1942; Holm-Jensen, Krogh and
Wartiovaara, 1944).

The most satisfactory investigations of ion movements between the external solution and the cytoplasm and vacuole of large algal cells have been made by MacRobbie and Dainty (1958) and by Diamond and Solomon (1959). The principle underlying both studies lay in bathing the cells—*Nitellopsis obtusa* (MacRobbie and Dainty), *Nitella axillaris* (Diamond and Solomon)—in solution containing radioactive isotopes and then measuring the rate at which the isotopes were lost when the cells were transferred to inactive solutions. The solutions used were such that there was no net change in the composition of the cell contents—MacRobbie and Dainty do not give evidence that this was so, but it is implicit in their choice of various ionic concentrations and in their demonstration of flux equilibria for the various ions between the various cellular compartments.

Both sets of data show that for potassium and sodium ions there are three phases in the loss of radioactivity from the cell corresponding to three compartments in the cell with distinct efflux rates. MacRobbie and Dainty identified the compartment showing the slowest rate of efflux with the vacuole. Their reasons for doing so were that the amounts of potassium, sodium and chloride in the slow fraction of a washing-out experiment corresponded with those estimated chemically in the sap and that the influx into the slow compartment does not differ significantly from the influx into the cell sap, determined by direct counting of samples of radioactive sap isolated from a labelled cell. Diamond and Solomon, using similar reasoning, made the same identification.

With *Nitellopsis*, when values for the rate of loss of radioactivity (for potassium, for instance) are plotted against time, an analysis of the resulting curve shows it to be the sum of two exponentials and a diffusion curve, or, approximately, the sum of three straight lines when the curve is plotted logarithmically. After subtracting the 'slowest' exponential, a curve is obtained which is the sum of an exponential and a very steep curve. The steep curve was identified as representing the loss of ions from the free space. This compartment shows a very rapid rate of exchange, and the rate of exchange is independent of temperature. Diamond and Solomon obtained a straight line, when the logarithm of the concentration of potassium in the fastest compartment was plotted against the logarithm of the external potassium concentration. The graph is characteristic of a Freundlich adsorption isotherm, indicating that potassium entry into this compartment is a physical phenomenon. The actual identity of this compartment will be discussed in the next chapter. The exponential phase was identified with the cytoplasm and was called by MacRobbie and Dainty 'protoplasmic non-free space'. Their determinations of the relative amounts of potassium and sodium in this compartment are of considerable interest. Ratios obtained from potassium and sodium determinations in different cells produce variable results. However, by determining the ratio on the same set of cells by using radioactive potassium and sodium simultaneously, it was possible to remove this variability. The cells were soaked in the solutions of the radioactive ions, and the amounts of the ions in the protoplasmic 'non-free' space were determined from washing out experiments. The results showed that there is twice as much potassium as sodium in this phase of the cytoplasm, whereas the external medium contains fifty times as much sodium as potassium. On the other hand, the K/Na ratio in the cytoplasmic compartment does not differ significantly from the K/Na ratio in the vacuole. This suggests that the potassium-sodium selectivity is a function of the protoplasmic non-free space. The ratio $(K + Na)/Cl$ is nearly ten times higher than the ratio for the vacuole, suggesting that the tonoplast is acting in a selective manner upon the chloride ion.

MacRobbie and Dainty calculated the ion concentration potentials which the ions should have, if the ions concerned moved passively under the action of the purely physical force of an electrochemical gradient. The calculated values were derived from the known concentrations of ions in the sap and the external solution and the application of the Nernst equation for the diffusion of ions across a membrane (see Chapter 2).*

The ion concentration potential differed for the three ions (potassium, sodium and chloride) whose concentration in the vacuolar sap was known. It was found that only potassium is in electrochemical equilibrium (Table 3). Both sodium and

* It should be emphasised that the Nernst equation applies only to equilibrium conditions. MacRobbie and Dainty, by showing that influx and efflux for each ion between the various compartments of the cell was equal, clearly demonstrated equilibrium conditions for the three ions under consideration.

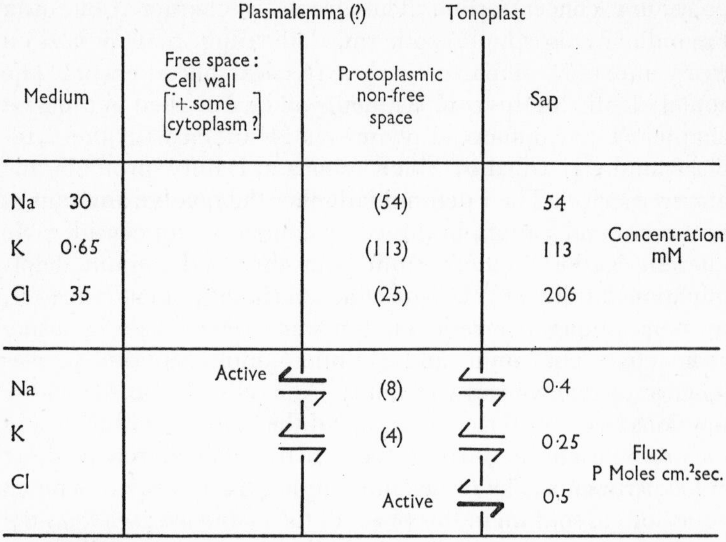

	Plasmalemma (?)		Tonoplast	
Medium	Free space: Cell wall [+.some cytoplasm?]	Protoplasmic non-free space	Sap	
Na 30		(54)	54	Concentration mM
K 0·65		(113)	113	
Cl 35		(25)	206	
Na	Active ⇄	(8)	⇄ 0·4	
K	⇄	(4)	⇄ 0·25	Flux P Moles cm.²sec.
Cl			Active ⇄ 0·5	

Fig. 3. A provisional scheme for the normal state of the cell of *Nitellopsis obtusa* showing ion concentrations within the two inner compartments and the ion fluxes across their boundaries. Protoplasmic figures, shown in parentheses, are uncertain, as the volume of the compartment is not accurately known (MacRobbie and Dainty, 1958).

chloride proved to be very far from their equilibrium distribution. These two ions must be actively transported—the former outwards and the latter inwards. The mechanism for active transport of sodium must be located somewhere in the cytoplasm, while that for chloride must be located in the tonoplast (Fig. 3).

TABLE 3

Ion concentration potentials (E) in the sap of *Nitellopsis obtusa* calculated from the Nernst equation

(MacRobbie and Dainty, 1958)

E in mV.

Ion	C_o/C_i	where $E = \dfrac{58}{z} \log \dfrac{C_o}{C_i}$
Na+	0·556	− 15
K+	0·00575	−130
Cl′	0·170	+ 45

E, from measurements, was found to range from 120 to 200 mV.

These conclusions have themselves been confirmed in a very elegant manner by Blount and Levedahl (1960). Their investigations were based on the principle that, if equilibrium conditions with respect to the diffusion of ions were established across the protoplasm, any movement of ions must be the result of active transport. The vacuolar sap of *Halicystis ovalis* was replaced by sea water and the electrical potential across the protoplasm was shunted to zero. Under these conditions, with sea water as the external medium, any current which flowed will be carried by the ions which are actively transported. The unidirectional movements of ions were determined by radio-active isotopes. With an isotope initially in the external medium, the rate of its appearance in the vacuole measures the rate of influx, and vice versa for the rate of efflux. ^{22}Na, ^{24}Na and ^{36}Cl were used as isotopes, and current measurements were made simultaneously with flux measurements. The isotopes were used separately; a double label technique was not employed. Both the fluxes and short-circuit current varied widely in different experiments, however varying in a similar manner. Comparisons were made on the basis of the flux as a percentage of the short-circuit current. It was found (Table 4) that the net efflux of sodium ions accounts for 39·2 per cent. of the short-circuit current, while the net influx of chloride ions accounts for 57·6 per cent. of the short-circuit current. Thus almost the entire short-circuit current must be carried by the net fluxes of these two ions brought about by active transport. Blount and Levedahl agreed with MacRobbie and Dainty that the active transport mechanism for sodium ions is located in the outer membrane, while that for chloride ions is located in the tonoplast.

These conclusions reinforce and amplify the earlier and very much more tentative conclusions of Blinks (1940) drawn from P.D. data obtained with *Halicystis*. Blinks (1930) also measured the direct current resistance across the cytoplasm of *Nitella* and obtained a value which agrees with a value for the electrical resistance between the vacuole and the external medium calculated by MacRobbie and Dainty from the tonoplast fluxes which they determined for *Nitellopsis*. Fluxes across the tonoplast are 20 to 100 times slower than across the outer surface of the cytoplasm in *Nitellopsis*. The tonoplast must

TABLE 4

Sodium flux, chloride flux and short-circuit current in cells of *Halicystis ovalis* with sea-water inside and out. Column 5 tabulates the percentage of the short-circuit current carried by the sodium flux or by the chloride flux

(Blount and Levedahl, 1960)

Ion	Number of Experiments	P.D. (mV.)	Flux p mol. per cm.² second	Short-circuit current μa per cm.²	$\dfrac{\mu a(\text{flux}) \times 100}{\mu a(\text{short})}$.
Na⁺	10 range mean	75–82 79	Efflux 16–226 74	4–38 13	40–59 48·7 S.D.=5·2
	8 range mean	75–81 79	Influx 6–20 10	8–14 10	6–14 9·5 S.D.=1·6 mean net efflux=39·2 S.D.=5·4
Cl′	10 range mean	76–84 80	Efflux 54–191 102	26–55 39	14–25 23·7 S.D.=3·7
	10 range mean	80–85 82	Influx 247–638 426	29–67 50	74–91 81·3 S.D.=3·7 mean net influx=57·6 S.D.=5·3

therefore be the site of the principle diffusion resistance of the cell. This conclusion does not agree with the findings of Walker (1957), who found that the major part (75 to 100 per cent.) of the d.c. resistance of the cell of *Nitella* lay between the cytoplasm and the outside medium. There is a further divergence between the two sets of data in that Walker found the measured specific resistance to be 6×10^3 ohms cm.^{2} compared with the calculated value of 250×10^3 ohm cm.^{2}. Bennett and Rideal (1954) found the a.c. resistance of *Nitella* to be 78×10^3 ohms cm.^{2}. These latter authors also believe the major part of the resistance of the cytoplasmic system lies in the external region of the cytoplasm. The evidence in favour of this view came from the decrease in the resistance associated with cell plasmolysis. It was assumed that plasmolysis, by removing the outer layers of protoplasm from the wall, increases the surface area of the interface between the protoplasm and the external medium. Since the tonoplast in the turgid cell is not in contact with a solid matrix such as the cell well, it was assumed that plasmolysis does not bring about so great a decrease in surface area at the interphase between cytoplasm and vacuole as between cytoplasm and the external medium. There is no direct evidence that such changes in area are involved, nor did Bennett and Rideal make any investigations on the reversibility of their resistance measurements with deplasmolysis.

Walker (1957) suggested that the differences in the resistances quoted above is due to different growth treatments given to the various cells. Briggs (1957a) pointed out that the conductivity of cytoplasm and tonoplast will depend on the concentration and mobility of anions in both these phases. The extent of pre-treatment must be important in this respect. Briggs also pointed out that the lower permeability of the tonoplast, compared with the rest of the cytoplasm does not necessarily allow the assumption that the major part of the resistance of the whole cytoplasm lies in the tonoplast. The resistance of the various layers will depend not only on their permeability but also upon their depth and upon the mobility of the anions residing within each layer.

In view of the fact that MacRobbie and Dainty found that potassium and sodium appear to be passively distributed across the tonoplast in approximately equal concentrations on both sides of the membrane, there should be only a small potential difference across this layer, and, in consequence, the main potential drop should be expected across the external protoplasmic membrane. The measurements of the P.D. between the external solution and the cytoplasm and the external solution and the vacuole of *Nitella* made by Walker (1955) support this conclusion. Using the same P.D. measurements, Walker (1957 and 1958) was able to show, as a result of an impossible calculated concentration of calcium in the cytoplasm of *Nitella*, that the cytoplasm must show some degree of impermeability to calcium.

The large algal cell can be considered as a three component system—each component characterised by distinct flux rates and permeability characteristics. The two slower compartments can be identified respectively with part of the cytoplasm and the vacuole. The fastest compartment can be identified with the free space of the cell—ions entering this compartment from the external medium by diffusion. On the other hand, ions may be actively transported into the other two compartments, though there seems to be a difference between the ions as to which are actively transported into the protoplasmic non-free space and which are actively transported into the vacuole. The experimental data concerning the physiology of the vacuole suggests that the concept of salts being secreted into the vacuole from the cytoplasm is misleading. Some ions are transported into the vacuole, but many of the observed characteristics of the vacuole may be due to the low permeability (in comparison to the outer surface of the cell) of the tonoplast. There is no evidence to suggest that ions are necessarily at a higher concentration in the vacuole than the rest of the cytoplasm.

An extended discussion of the location and properties of the free space of cells other than algal cells will be given in the next chapter. The free space has a similar range of properties for a wide range of cells, including large algal cells. It is only with large algal cells that observed movements of ions within the cell can be identified with certainty as movements of ions between the vacuole and the cytoplasm. This does not mean that non-free space of other cells cannot be subdivided into compartments. There is good evidence that this in fact is possible, but there is little evidence to identify these physiological phases with structural entities.

Perhaps the most positive evidence that the vacuole exerts an effect on the ionic relations of plant cells, other than the large algal cells described above, comes from the work of Sutcliffe and Counter (1959), who studied differences in ion uptake brought about by growth changes in storage tissues induced by coconut milk. This growth substance results in the tissue becoming meristematic, with a decrease in the vacuolar content. Changes in the rate of ion uptake observed after treatment of the tissue with coconut milk may therefore be attributable to a decrease in the proportion of cells containing vacuoles as a result of the increased rate of growth. Sutcliffe and Counter studied the uptake of potassium and sodium by discs of carrot and red beet left for two or three weeks with and without coconut milk. They found that tissues treated with coconut milk absorb more potassium and less sodium per gm. fresh weight than untreated tissues. The ratio of potassium to sodium absorbed increases as a result of treating the tissues with coconut milk. Sutcliffe and Counter suggested that the cytoplasm exerts a selective effect upon the potassium-sodium balance of the cell in favour of potassium, while the tonoplast is more selective for sodium than potassium. The cytoplasm could exert its effect by removing sodium from the cell.

Evidence that higher plant cells must be considered as multi-component systems with relation to dissolved substances comes from a variety of sources. Arisz (1958) investigated the effect of inhibitors on the uptake and transport of chloride ions in the leaves of *Vallisneria spiralis*. He used leaf lengths which were 7·5 cm. in length and 4 mm. in width. Eight of these strips were used in an experiment. 2·5 cm. of tissue at one end of each strip was placed in contact with the salt whose uptake was to be studied. After the experimental period, the strips were divided into three and analysed for chloride. Addition of 10^{-5} M sodium azide to the salt solution, while reducing the absorption of chloride in the absorption zone, in no way prevents considerable quantities of chloride being accumulated in the other two zones. Equally, treatment of the middle zone with the same concentration of sodium azide, while preventing the accumulation of chloride within the zone, does not prevent the chloride accumulation within the third zone from reaching a level not very dissimilar from that reached in the third zone of untreated controls. 10^{-4} M potassium cyanide, if applied to the absorbing zone, not only prevents accumulation of chloride within the same zone but also considerably reduces the accumulation of chloride within the other two zones. When the same concentration of cyanide is applied to the middle zone, accumulation of chloride in all three zones is completely unaffected. Azide, at the concentrations used, must prevent chloride from accumulating within the cells of *Vallisneria* but does not prevent the chloride from being taken up by the cells, nor does it prevent the chloride from being transported from cell to cell. Cyanide must prevent chloride from being taken up but has no effect upon chloride accumulation. Arisz, from this evidence, postulated that chloride is first taken into the cytoplasm and then either accumulated in the vacuole or transferred from cell to cell via the symplasm (the continuous plasm constituting the cytoplasm of the cell and its interconnections with other cells (Arisz, 1945 and 1956)). Whether or not there is this correlation between the physiological facts and the structure of *Vallisneria* cells, it is clear that there are at least two components within the cell which possess different permeability properties to chloride ions.

The tonoplast in large algal cells is relatively impermeable to ions compared with the external surface of the cytoplasm. A similarly impermeable barrier round vacuoles can be invoked to explain certain metabolic phenomena observed with higher plant tissues. Bennet-Clark and Bexon (1943) observed that malate supplied to discs of beet, in concentrations very much lower than those prevalent in the vacuolar sap, accelerates the rate of respiration of the discs. Two suggestions were given to explain the results. One of their suggestions is that those respiratory enzymes whose activity is affected by malic acid may be located on the outside surface of the protoplast, with the result that a lower concentration at this surface may be more effective than a higher one on the inside surface. Alternatively, the external cytoplasmic membrane was postulated to have a greater permeability than the vacuolar boundary membrane. A similar explanation can be given for the results of D. H. Jennings (unpublished data) in which feeding of ammonium chloride to beech roots has no effect upon the level of orthophosphate within the root but markedly influences the metabolism of orthophosphate fed to the roots in the presence of ammonium chloride.

Diamond and Solomon showed, in agreement with the data of Mercer, Hodge, Hope and McLean (1955), that potassium readily distributes across the membrane of chloroplasts. Chloroplasts extracted from *Nitella* and placed in a medium containing ^{42}K contained as much isotope after six minutes, when the earliest samples were taken, as after several hours or even a day. Diamond and Solomon concluded that the chloroplast-cytoplasm layer, although structurally inhomogeneous, appears as a single compartment with regard to potassium. This observation is a salutary reminder that conclusions about permeability barriers should not be drawn solely from visual evidence. On the other hand, while permeability barriers cannot always be associated with cytoplasmic discontinuities, there is ample evidence from yeast that the cytoplasm possesses more than one permeability barrier to substances in the external medium (Rothstein, 1956). Experiments on the acid inactivation of cell surface enzymes provide evidence on this point. Mild acid destroys the invertase activity (Myrbäck and Willstaedt, 1955) and phosphatase activity (Rothstein, 1956) but has little effect on the fermentative activity. The former enzymes are directly accessible to the hydrogen ions of the medium. The fermentative enzymes themselves are sensitive to acid, so in the cell they must be protected by a barrier. Stronger acid will however reduce the fermentative activity of the cell. In this case, protection is afforded by extracellular potassium ions. Respiratory enzymes appear to be unaffected by these treatments, suggesting the presence of another permeability barrier.

The need to interpret such data as these in terms of a number of permeability barriers arises in part from the acceptance of a membrane whose dimensions may be much smaller than the actual permeability barrier which is present in plant cells. It has been customary to think in terms of a membrane 60 to 70 Å in thickness—the thickness of that membrane bounding the cytoplasm which is observed with the aid of the electron microscope. It has already been pointed out in Chapter 2 that care must be taken in equating morphological and physiological membranes, so that the observed thickness of the

D

plasmalemma may bear little relation to the thickness of the permeability barrier surrounding the cell. It is perhaps of significance in this respect that Frei and Preston (1961) require an outer layer to the cell of at least 500 Å thickness to account for the observed arrangement of cellulose microfibrils in the walls of *Cladophora rupestris* and *Chaetomorpha melagonium*. The results of Rothstein described above might be more readily explained in terms of a membrane of such thickness.

CHAPTER 4

THE FREE SPACE OF PLANT TISSUES

Briggs and Robertson (1948) pointed out that in discs of plant tissue, with intercellular spaces injected with water, the resistance offered to the passage of carbon dioxide is not very different from that of a layer of water of equal dimensions, but, for larger molecules such as sucrose and electrolytes, the movement of these substances is restricted to a small fraction of the path. Measurements of the potential difference between solutions of different concentrations separated by the disc showed that the P.D. is such as to suggest that the path of movement of an electrolyte through the tissue contains non-mobile anions. In a later paper (Briggs and Robertson, 1957) they amplify this concept of a phase within the tissue in which solutes can move relatively freely. It is in this paper that the implications of the concept of 'free space' are fully discussed. Although the term 'free space' was implicit in the earlier work of Briggs and Robertson, it was first used by Hope and Stevens (1952), though they acknowledged their debt to the Cambridge School for the original formulation of the term. Subsequently, the term has had frequent usage (Butler, 1953a; Hylmo, 1953; Hope, 1953).

Conway and Downey (1950) concluded, from their observations upon the appearance of succinic acid in the medium during the fermentation of glucose by yeast and from the diffusion of succinic acid into the cell, that this compound, although it is not able to diffuse into the whole cell, does enter some real space within the yeast cell. This space, which they called 'the outer region', occupies about 10 per cent. of the total cell volume. Molecules such as inulin, gelatine and peptone are unable to enter the outer region. These substances were therefore used to determine the volume of the intercellular space of centrifuged yeast. On the other hand, organic acids, sugars such as glucose, arabinose and galactose and potassium and sodium chlorides are able to enter the outer region rapidly.

Of the various substances tested, only monobasic fatty acids are able to penetrate rapidly throughout the cell.

In order to correlate the outer region of yeast cells with the free space of plant tissues, a comparison must be made between centrifuged yeast and not with isolated cells. The free space of plant tissues would then be equivalent to the outer region of yeast cells and the intercellular volume, which Conway and Downey measured either by removing under pressure the intercellular water or with the aid of those substances, such as inulin, which do not penetrate the outer region. This point is made at the present stage of the discussion of the concept of free space, for the term 'outer space' has been used to define the total free space of roots by Epstein (1955). This is unfortunate, for the correspondence is not exact and the outer space of yeast cells is more likely to be equivalent to the Donnan space of higher plant tissues. It seems wise to restrict the term 'outer space' to unicellular organisms.

The term 'free space' is concerned with tissues and should in actual fact be considered as a theoretical term. The term 'apparent free space' or A.F.S. concerns experimental estimates and emphasises the approximate nature of such estimates made with a system whose limits are not completely known. Briggs and Robertson (1957) adopted the following definition for A.F.S. 'If U is the estimated amount of free space uptake of solute by tissue originally devoid of this solute from a solution of concentration C, the A.F.S. is U/C.' The definition emphasises that the A.F.S. is a function of the solute used in its measurement. The A.F.S. is in reality that volume which at equilibrium contains solute at the same concentration as in the external solution. The relationship between A.F.S. and free space will depend on the solute used for the determination. There is a complementary term to free space, which refers to that part of the tissue which is not freely available to the external solution, namely the osmotic volume and its experimental counterpart, apparent osmotic volume or A.O.V.

There are a variety of methods for determining the size of the free space (Briggs and Robertson, 1957; Briggs, 1957b). A relatively simple method (in so far as it requires very little by way of apparatus) relies on weighing the tissue in water, in the solution and in air (with necessary correction for drift due to penetration into the non-free space and loss of weight due to respiration). From the weights of tissue in water (W_w), in solution (W_s) and in air (W_a), the final volume of the tissue and the A.O.V. can be calculated. Thus the final volume of tissue (V)

$$= \frac{W_a - W_s}{\Delta_s},$$

and the A.O.V. $\qquad = \dfrac{W_w - W_s}{\Delta_s - \Delta_w}.$

Therefore, the A.F.S. $= V -$ A.O.V.,

where $\qquad \Delta_s$ = the density of the solutions and

Δ_w = that of water.

There are two major points of experimental method which must be emphasised, since they apply to all methods of determination. When tissues are submerged, the intercellular air spaces gradually decrease in size due to the disappearance of carbon dioxide into solution. To overcome this, it is best if the air within the tissue is removed by evacuation. Second, the osmotic strength of the solution used has an important bearing on the determination of the size of the free space. If more than a certain strength of solution is used, the cells lose turgor and the tissue behaves as an osmometer.

More generally, the methods which are used depend on the direct determination of solute penetration into the free space. The ease with which penetration can be measured with radio-active isotopes makes these methods particularly applicable to determinations using inorganic ions. The advantage of such methods lies in the fact that low temperatures can be more conveniently employed to prevent drifts due to penetration into the non-free space. This factor of penetration into the non-free space can of course be removed, if a solute is chosen which does not penetrate the non-free space even at normal temperatures. Such a solute should give identical values for the A.F.S., independently of the time in which the tissue is in the solution subsequent to equilibration with the free space, and also independently of the concentration of solute when there is no loss of turgor. The independence from concentration also demonstrates that the solute is not adsorbed on any structure within the free space—it is unlikely that adsorption is proportional to concentration over a wide range. Under these circumstances, the concentration in the free space is then the same as the external solution. The uptake of solute will then give a measure of the A.F.S. Butler (1953b) showed that mannitol behaves in this manner and determined the A.F.S. of wheat roots with this solute. He determined the uptake of mannitol by allowing the roots to equilibrate with the external solution, then transferred the roots, after blotting, to a solution containing no mannitol, when the amount diffusing out could be measured.

With electrolytes the situation is more complex, for the free space cannot be considered as a homogeneous system with respect to ions. In the presence of an electrolyte, the free space appears to be composed of at least two components—'the water phase' (Briggs, Hope and Pitman, 1958a) and 'the Donnan system' (Briggs and Robertson, 1957). Leaving aside any consideration of the location of these two components, the water phase is extremely simple physiologically and can be considered as that phase into which substance diffuse unimpeded, and, at equilibrium, the actual concentration within the phase is the same as the external solution.

The Donnan system is that part of the tissue available to the external solution which is under the influence of non-mobile anions. A Donnan system is one in which certain of the ions within it have their movement restricted, either by the impermeability of a membrane, or by the fact that the ion is joined by a chemical bond to an insoluble structure.

The following situation can be considered:

$$
\begin{array}{c|c}
A^+{}_o & A^+{}_i \\
\text{outside} \quad\quad & \quad\quad \text{inside} \\
B'{}_o & B'{}_i \\
& A^+{}_i \, X'
\end{array}
$$

interface

There is in this system a non-mobile anion X' which is associated with the cation A^+ and a solution of the salt AB, all being inside an interface. Outside the interface there is another solution of AB. The interface can be considered as a membrane impermeable to X', where X' is free to move in aqueous solution, or it can be considered as the extent of the influence of the charge of X' when the anion is attached to an insoluble structure.

Initially, the concentration of AB outside can be made equal to the concentration of AB inside. There will however be an inequality of A^+ on the two sides of the interface, with a greater number inside owing to the association with X' as well as B'. Since there is this inequality, A^+ will tend to diffuse from inside to outside. But, since A^+ cannot be accompanied by X', a potential difference will be generated. The solution outside will now be electrically positive to the solution inside, and this will draw B' out of the inside solution into the outside solution. Movement of B' will occur until an activity gradient in the opposite direction is established, which is large enough for movement at the same rate in the reverse direction. No further change will then take place; the system will be in electro-chemical equilibrium.

Since the system is in electro-chemical equilibrium, the Nernst equation can be applied to the system. The following relationships will hold.

$$\Delta E = RT \ln \frac{aA^+_i}{aA^+_o} = -RT \ln \frac{aB'_i}{aB'_o},$$

thus,
$$\frac{aA^+_i}{aA^+_o} = \frac{aB'_o}{aB'_i}$$

This is the Donnan (or Gibbs-Donnan) equilibrium.

This equilibrium can be extended to any other ions which are free to move in the system. For the above system, since consideration has been given only to univalent ions, the charge of the ions has been neglected. However, if there are mobile ions of differing charge within the system, the charge (z) of each species must be taken into consideration. With two cations, A_1 and A_2, having different charges, the following relationship will hold:

$$\frac{(aA_1)_i^{\frac{1}{z_1}}}{(aA_1)_o^{\frac{1}{z_1}}} = \frac{(aA_2)_i^{\frac{1}{z_2}}}{(aA_2)_o^{\frac{1}{z_2}}}.$$

If A_1 is univalent and A_2 is bivalent, then

$$\frac{(aA_1)_i}{(aA_1)_o} = \frac{\sqrt{(aA_2)_i}}{\sqrt{(aA_2)_o}},$$

or

$$\frac{(aA_1)_i^2}{(aA_1)_o^2} = \frac{(aA_2)_i}{(aA_2)_o}.$$

It should be noted that mobile anions in the external solution will only be able to enter a Donnan system containing non-mobile anions when the charge of these latter ions is neutralised by cations.

The most convenient way of describing the experimental procedure for measuring the number of non-mobile ions in the free space is by recourse to a published account of an actual determination. Briggs, Hope and Pitman (1958a) have made one of the most reliable determinations of the size of the water-free space and the Donnan system using discs of red beet. They gave their experimental material a standard treatment, such that the status of the cations associated with the non-mobile cations was completely known. The standard treatment consisted of six periods of thirty minutes' duration, during which the discs were aerated in a solution of the same cation at a prescribed strength, and at the end of which the discs were transferred to a fresh solution. At the end of this treatment, either rubidium ions or calcium ions were the only cations associated with the Donnan system of the discs. Using low temperatures $(2°)$ and low concentrations of salt in the experimental solutions, they studied the exchange of cations between the free space of such pretreated discs and the external medium which contained the radioactive ions. Since they were using low concentrations, Briggs et al. were able to measure the water phase of the free space by the use of an anion, in this case [131]I. Under these conditions, where rubidium ions are the sole cation associated with the free space, the number of exchangeable cations associated with the non-mobile anions and hence the number of these latter ions can be determined by measuring the extra exchangeable ^{86}Rb over and above that associated with anions in the water-free space. This gives the number of non-mobile anions per kg. of tissue. This cannot be converted to a concentration in the Donnan free space unless the volume of the free space itself is known.

The easiest way to determine this volume is through an estimation of the extra exchangeable ^{86}Rb, when the sole cations associated with the Donnan system are bivalent; in the experiments being described, these ions were calcium. Under these conditions, an equilbirium is set up such that

$$\frac{[\mathrm{Ca}_i]}{[\mathrm{Ca}_o]} = \frac{[\mathrm{Rb}_i]^2}{[\mathrm{Rb}_o]^2}.$$

Now under the experimental conditions, the concentration of calcium chloride used for washing the discs during the pre-treatment was the same as the concentration of rubidium chloride (in m.equiv. per l.) used for measuring the exchange of ions. This being so, the following equations hold.

For calcium ions the amount of calcium in the discs before the treatment with the rubidium chloride solution can be equated with that in the discs plus that in the medium after the new equilibrium is reached.

Thus $V_W C_o + V_D A = (V_o + V_W)\mathrm{Ca}_o + V_D \mathrm{Ca}_i,$

where V_D, V_W and V_o are the volumes of the Donnan system, the water free space and the external solution respectively. C_o is the total concentration outside.

For rubidium ions

$$V_o C_o = V_D \mathrm{Rb}_i + (V_W + V_o)\mathrm{Rb}_o.$$

If $V_D A = a$ and $V_D \mathrm{Rb}_i = X$, and since $A = \mathrm{Ca}_i + \mathrm{Rb}_i$, the equation for calcium ions can be written

$$\mathrm{Ca}_o = \frac{V_W C_o + X}{V_o + V_W}.$$

That for rubidium ions can be written

$$\mathrm{Rb}_o = \frac{V_o C_o - X}{V_W - V_o}.$$

Substituting for Ca_o and Rb_o and for Ca_i and Rb_i (when $\mathrm{Ca}_i = \dfrac{a-X}{V_D}$ and $\mathrm{Rb}_i = \dfrac{X}{V_D}$) in the equilibrium relationship,

$$\frac{[\mathrm{Ca}_i]}{[\mathrm{Ca}_o]} = \frac{[\mathrm{Rb}_i]^2}{[\mathrm{Rb}_o]^2},$$

we get

$$V_D = (V_o + V_W) \cdot \frac{X^2}{(V_o C_o - X)} \cdot \frac{(V_W C_o + X)}{(a - X)} .$$

From the experimental measurements, the water phase was found to occupy 15 to 20 per cent. of the volume of 1 mm. thick beetroot slices. Using the above relationship, the Donnan phase was found to be 2 to 3 per cent. of the tissue volume. The concentration of non-mobile anions was estimated to be 560 m. equiv. per l. of the Donnan system (Fig. 4 for experimental results).

There have been estimates for a variety of tissues of the number of non-mobile anions, but these estimates have not been expressed in terms of the volume of the Donnan system. To do this, it is necessary to make an estimate of the volume of the Donnan phase. Briggs and Robertson (1957) have calculated the concentration of non-mobile anions within the free space of carrot discs using the results of Stiles and Skelding (1940), who studied the uptake of manganous sulphate. The counter ions in the Donnan phase were assumed to be bivalent, and, if the Donnan phase occupied as much as 5 per cent. of the tissue, the concentration of non-mobile anions is 400 to 600 m.equiv. per l.

The only comparable determination to that made by Briggs *et al.* of the volume of the Donnan phase has been made with the alga *Chara australis* by Dainty and Hope (1959). The concentration of non-mobile anions in the Donnan system of the large cells of this alga was estimated to be 400 to 600 m.equiv. per l.

The interaction between cations in the external solution and non-mobile anions in the free space has been deliberately referred to as being Donnan in nature. Nevertheless, there is not general agreement on this point. Epstein and Leggett (1954), Epstein (1955) and Sutcliffe (1957) have described the relationship between the cations in the external solution and non-mobile anions in the free space as being one of 'binding'. Those authors who have interpreted their results in terms of a process of 'binding' have pointed out the similarity between such binding phenomena and the affinity of anionic exchange resins for cations in the surrounding solutions. Perhaps the term 'binding' is unfortunate; nevertheless there is not complete evidence that all equilibria between mobile cations and non-

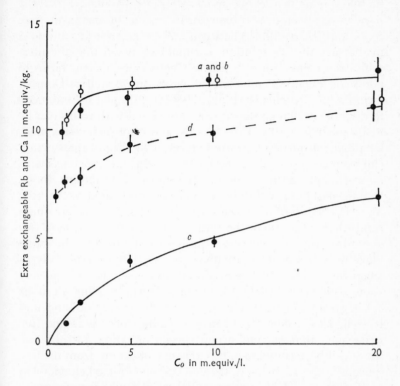

Fig. 4. Data of Briggs, Hope and Pitman (1958a) showing some characteristics of the D.F.S. of beet discs as the result of various pretreatments:

(a) Closed circles. Extra exchangeable rubidium in tissue pretreated with rubidium.

(b) Open circles. Extra exchangeable calcium in tissue pretreated with calcium.

(c) Extra exchangeable rubidium in tissue pretreated with calcium. The line indicates theoretical values for X as a function of C_o.

(d) Extra exchangeable rubidium in tissue not pretreated to ensure complete removal of the bivalent cations.

The rise in curve (a) from 10 to 12·7 as C_o rises from 1 to 20 m. equiv. per L. might be due to an increase in A due to an increase in ionization of an acid HA.

mobile anions in the free space is strictly Donnan. Since the parallel has been drawn between behaviour of ions in the free space and the equilibria between ion-exchange resins and ions in the surrounding solution, it should be noted that the most sound representation must include activity coefficient terms to allow for 'chemical' interaction of the ions as well as Donnan formulation (Kitchener, 1957). However, simpler formulations to describe exchange phenomena associated with resins can be made solely in terms of the binding power of such resins, and, for practical purposes, a simple form of the law of mass action can be used to calculate the ionic equilibrium associated with ion-exchange resins and the solutions surrounding them. Whatever the suitability of the various terms used to describe the relationship of ions in the free space, there is an adequate rationale for the use of the term 'binding', and the use of this term and that of Donnan equilibrium to denote the same phenomenon are not mutually exclusive. This is especially so when the activity of ions inside the free space is incompletely known. One can criticise the use of the term 'binding' in so far as suggestions of ion-exchange are excluded (Middleton and Russell, 1958). There is always a balance of ions in the free space such that entry of a new species of cation into the free space will be accompanied by exchange of cations from the free space. On the other hand, the description of ionic behaviour in the free space solely in terms of Donnan equilibrium excludes considerations which involve the relative affinities of the non-mobile anions for the external cations. So very little is known about the nature of the non-mobile anions in the free space that the use of the term 'Donnan space' may eventually be restricting. Referring to the analogy between free space phenomena and ion-exchange resin phenomena, the affinity of various resins for certain ions differs from resin to resin and cannot be interpreted in terms of the properties of the cations alone or even the cation-anion interaction (Kitchener, 1957). Clearly, a possible approach to the determination of the characteristics and proportion of the non-mobile anions in the free space could follow similar lines, whereby the selectivity of the anions for a range of cations could be determined.

In fact, although the number of non-mobile anions in the free space has been determined, little is known concerning the exact nature of these ions in higher plant tissues. There is even disagreement over the location of the fixed anionic groups. Certain workers favour the cytoplasm as the site where these fixed ions are found (Butler, 1953a; Sutcliffe, 1954; Lundegårdh, 1955; Briggs and Robertson, 1957), while others favour the cell wall (Williams and Coleman, 1950; Dainty and Hope, 1959; Diamond and Solomon, 1959; Laties, 1959a). The evidence for the location of the fixed ions in the cell wall comes from those comparisons between the ion exchange capacity of isolated cell walls and the free space characteristics of whole cells. Large algal cells allow the greatest ease of comparison. Isolated cell walls of *Nitella axillaris* were obtained by Diamond and Solomon (1959), by cutting off both ends of the cell and pushing out the vacuole and cytoplasm together with the chloroplasts, while Dainty and Hope (1959) obtained isolated cell walls by cutting open cells of *Chara australis* and gently scraping the wall to remove the contents. With the cells of both species, it was possible to show that the ion exchange characteristics of the fastest exchanging compartments are extremely similar to the ion exchange characteristics of isolated cell walls. Laties (1959a) quotes the evidence of Jansen, Albersheim and Bonner, who estimated the cation exchange capacity of fresh sections of oat coleoptiles and compared the value which they obtained with the exchanging capacity of wall material. The two values agree remarkably well. There is equal agreement when the base exchange capacity of fresh coleoptile sections is compared with the exchange capacity of wall material calculated in terms of pectin free carboxyl groups in the wall, from which it was concluded that these groups provide non-mobile anions within the free space.

Those who uphold the cytoplasmic location of non-mobile anions have not provided any comparable evidence in favour of their view. Briggs, Hope and Pitman (1958a) point out that, if the Donnan phase is identified with the cytoplasm, the number of non-mobile anions is 600 m.equiv. per l. and the counterions monovalent, the phase will have an osmotic pressure of about eleven atmospheres, provided that the activity of the counterions was similar to that in aqueous solution. While this means that the solution in the cytoplasm is under the same hydrostatic pressure as the vacuole (which has been shown to be eleven atmospheres from observations at incipient plasmolysis), this state of affairs need not hold. Should the monovalent cations be replaced by bivalent ions, then the osmotic pressure of the cytoplasm will change, since the O.P. is a function of molarity and not of the number of equivalents. While the experiments of Briggs, Hope and Pitman were not precise enough to detect a change in the volume of the cytoplasm accompanying these changes, it is obvious that this phenomena must be rigorously checked if any hypothesis concerning the location of the non-mobile anions is to be held with any degree of certainty.

Perhaps at this stage it would be wise to turn to those studies concerning the interaction between uranyl ions and the yeast cell (Rothstein, 1954). These studies provide another viewpoint from which to consider the nature of the non-mobile anions. Uranium in solution rapidly equilibrates with the yeast cell, as much uranium being bound after one minute as after 30 minutes. Yeast cells can bind uranium up to a concentration of 1×10^{-3} M per l. of cells. When cells are exposed to 2×10^{-5} M uranium, there is 90 per cent. inhibition of glucose uptake. This inhibitory action of uranium provides a means of studying the degree of binding of uranium by the yeast cell, for, if the binding of uranium by the cell is reduced, the inhibition is likewise reduced.

The action of uranium on metabolism is restricted to an inhibition of hexose metabolism (Rothstein, Meier and Hurwitz, 1951). There is no effect on the respiration of alcohol or pyruvate and very little effect on the respiration of acetate and lactate. Nor is there any effect on endogenous respiration as measured by oxygen consumption or glycogen depletion. Uranium specifically blocks the uptake of hexose sugars by the yeast cell. There is no effect on the metabolism of the sugars once they have entered the yeast cell. Of the metabolic sequences involving glucose within the yeast cell, fermentation is the most sensitive to the inhibition of glucose uptake by uranium poisoning.

The site of action of uranium appears to be at the cell surface, only a very small fraction of the uranium associated with the yeast cell passing into the cytoplasm. Addition of 2×10^{-4} M orthophosphate to uranium-poisoned suspensions of yeast reduces the inhibition of glucose uptake from 90 to 30 per cent. In view of the fact that the cytoplasm already contains 1×10^{-2} M orthophosphate, fifty times as high as the medium, the uranium must be bound at a location in the cell which is accessible to the phosphate of the medium rather than the phosphate of the cytoplasm. This and similar observations indicate the reversible nature of the binding of uranium to yeast, which can be characterised by a single reversible reaction

$$U + \Upsilon = U\Upsilon,$$

where U refers to the concentration of free uranyl ions, Υ to the number of unbound sites and $U\Upsilon$ to the concentration of uranium bound to the yeast cell. This equation can be tested in the form

$$K = \frac{(U)(\Upsilon)}{(U\Upsilon)}.$$

Rothstein, Frenkel and Larrabee (1948) showed that there is a direct proportionality between the number of sites which are combined with uranium and the inhibition of fermentation, with essentially 100 per cent. inhibition of metabolism when $4 \cdot 6 \times 10^{7}$ molecules are taken up by each cell. Over a twenty-fold range of total uranium concentration (within the limits of those concentrations inhibiting fermentation) K, which can be calculated by means of the mass action equilibrium, remains relatively constant. This and other evidence indicates that uranium forms a dissociable complex in a one to one ratio with certain active groups on the surface of the cell. The dissociation constant of these 'groups' associated with fermentation is about 4×10^{-7} M.

Rothstein and Meier (1951) attempted to determine the chemical nature of those uranium binding sites associated with fermentation. They did this by using a test system which consisted of a fixed amount of yeast, a fixed concentration of uranium and a variable concentration of each complexing agent and measuring the amount of uranium which was retained in the supernate as the result of competition between the complexing agent and the yeast cell for the uranyl ion. Of all the classes of agent tested, only the multiphosphate has a stability of the same order of magnitude as that of the yeast-uranium complex. The compounds which most resemble the cell in this respect are the metaphosphate polymers of high molecular weight. Polyphosphates appear to be chemically similar to yeast surface sites, not only because the complex which they form with uranium possesses the same order of stability, but also because they are influenced by pH in the same manner.

The sites associated with fermentation form the most stable complex with uranium. The presence of uranium concentration greater than that required for complete inhibition of fermentation leads to further uranium uptake, amounting to at least 3×10^7 sites per cell and perhaps more. The complex formed under these conditions is relatively unstable, requiring high concentrations to achieve saturation. These 'unstable' sites appear to be carboxyl in nature and appear to be involved in the respiration of glucose by non-fermentative pathways, for a concentration of uranium which gives essentially complete inhibition of fermentation results in only 60 per cent. inhibition of respiration. The inhibition of the remainder of the respiration requires a very much higher uranium concentration.

Whatever the exact meaning of the term 'cell surface' (Rothstein and Meier (1948) emphasise that it is not used in a strict mathematical sense but in the sense that there is a barrier to the interchange of phosphate—and, one imagines, any other compound—between the medium and the aqueous phase of the cytoplasm), the implications of the above work are clearly apparent. The uranyl ion must enter some space within the yeast cell freely available to the external solution. Is one to conclude that the sites which 'bind' uranium to the yeast cell surface are equivalent to the non-mobile anions associated with the Donnan phase of higher plant tissues? There is some reason for believing that this conclusion is partly correct.

The concentration of binding sites which firmly bind manganese to yeast cells is the same as those which firmly bind uranium (Rothstein and Hayes, 1956). Manganese competes with uranium for surface sites, and further evidence of the surface location for those sites which bind manganous ions comes from the marked influence of extracellular pH. Other bivalent and monovalent ions compete for the same sites. Rothstein and Hayes, by assuming that (like uranium) the equilibrium between manganous ions and the yeast cell is of the form

$$M + Y = MY$$

and deriving a mass-action relationship from this, showed that there are at least two species of binding site for manganous ions of differing affinity. The number of sites with the highest affinity for manganese is the same as those associated with the inhibition of fermentation by uranium. Other bivalent cations such as magnesium, calcium, strontium and cupric ions all competed with manganous ions for the binding sites and form a complex with the cellular groups that is of the same order of stability as the Mn^{++} complex. Thus the bivalent cations frequently used for free space studies can become associated with polyphosphate and carboxyl groups at the cell surface.

While studies on isolated cell walls provide strong evidence for the location of the fixed anions, such studies provide no definite evidence concerning their chemical nature. Cellulose and pectic materials are prime candidates, if the free space resides in the cell wall. Dainty and Hope (1959) point out that cytoplasmic contamination of isolated walls cannot be avoided. This appears to be confirmed by Diamond and Solomon (1959), who obtained an unaccountably low level of radioactivity in isolated cytoplasm when they were studying the compartmentalisation of the cell to ^{42}K. They concluded that some cytoplasm must remain attached to the cell wall, which suggests that their criterion of visual homogeneity of the wall is not paralleled by physiological homogeneity. On this evidence, it seems that groups other than those classically associated with cell walls must not be excluded from considerations of the free space.

The problem resolves itself into an evaluation of the proportion of the various molecular species contributing to the fixed anions of the free space. Demis, Rothstein and Meier (1954) showed that uranium at very much higher concentrations than those which blocked fermentation is bound to the carboxyl groups of invertase at the cell surface as well as with the polyphosphate groups associated with the fermentation of glucose. In fact, invertase activity is found to be only one-tenth as sensitive to uranium as the fermentation of glucose. Harley and Smith (1956) and Harley and Jennings (1958) found that

E

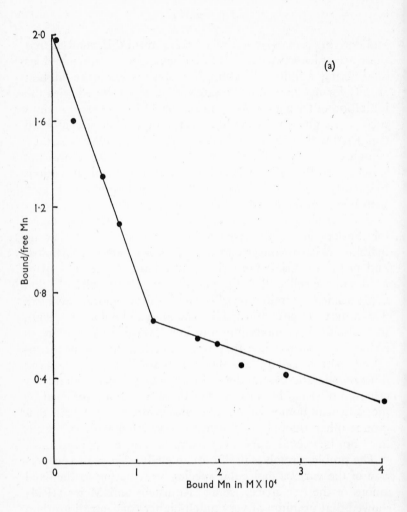

Fig. 5(a). Data for the binding of manganous ions by yeast cells plotted according to the mass-action relationship discussed on page 54. (Rothstein and Hayes, 1956).

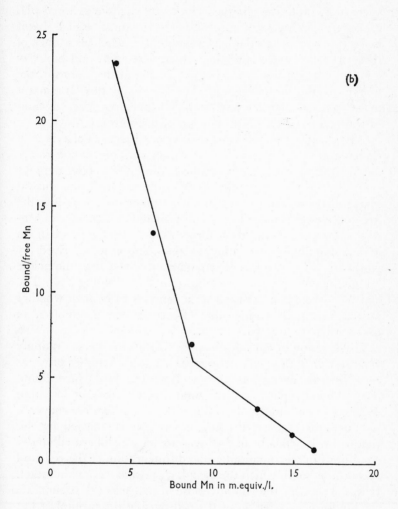

FIG. 5(b). Data for beet discs (from Stiles and Skelding, 1940) plotted in a similar manner.

sugar uptake and invertase activity of *Peltigera polydactyla* and beech mycorrhizal roots respectively are similarly sensitive to silver ions. From the observed marked changes of external pH, the location of invertase in these two tissues must be such that it is freely accessible to the external solution. The cell surface of these tissues must be similar to yeast, and one could be fairly safe in assuming that a certain proportion of the anions in the free space are polyphosphate and carboxyl in nature. It remains to be seen whether the fixed anions in the free space of non-fungal tissues contain a proportion of these groups.

When a plant tissue is titrated with a base, it behaves as if there were a succession of acidic groups with decreasing values of K_a (Briggs, 1957b). Stiles and Skelding (1940) offer data for red beet which is comparable to that obtained by Rothstein and Hayes for yeast, namely the uptake of manganous ions into the free space of beet root discs over a range of manganese concentrations. Fig. 5 shows data for yeast and beet plotted in an identical manner, according to the relationship derived by Rothstein and Hayes. This comparison shows that the acidic groups in the free space can be treated as binding sites. The logical outcome of this is clear; it remains to be seen whether uranyl ions have comparable effects on the metabolism of tissues other than yeast.

The location of enzymes in the cell wall has been strikingly expressed in a practical manner as a result of studies on yeast cells. Burger, Bacon and Bacon (1958 and 1961) have found that a large proportion of the total invertase may be lost from living yeast cells under the influence of snail digestive enzymes, although the viable cell count is virtually unaffected by this treatment. Practically all the invertase may be 'liberated' under conditions in which considerable disintegration of the cell wall takes place but in which the escaping protoplasts remain intact. It was concluded that the invertase of the yeast cell occurs in a soluble form in a region of the cell outside the protoplast but inside the cell wall. Friis and Ottolenghi (1959a and b) have confirmed these observations and have shown that cells adapted to ferment melibiose have their melibiase also located in association with cell wall material.

Chapter 5

THE RELATION BETWEEN SALT ABSORPTION AND METABOLISM

It is fair to say that the present realisation of the importance of the link between salt absorption and metabolism in plant tissues owes its foundation to the conclusions of Hoagland and Davis (1929). Other authors may have pointed out previously that this relationship might exist, but none were as emphatic in maintaining the necessity of such a linkage in salt absorption— particularly in salt accumulation. Hoagland and Davis found that the sap of *Nitella* is twenty-five times more concentrated than that of the pond water in which it was growing and they concluded that, if, and there was no reason to doubt this, the electrolytes in the sap are dissociated, then the plant cell must perform work in absorbing ions.

Since 1929 there have been two major hypotheses concerning the relation of salt absorption and metabolism in higher plant cells. These two hypotheses—the one postulated by Steward and the other by Lundegårdh—have been based on the observed connection between the respiratory behaviour of tissues and the ability of the same tissues to absorb salts, rather than on any strict energy considerations. Since this is so, if the part played by metabolism in salt absorption is to be determined, the facts on which these two hypotheses have been based must always be considered independently of any considerations concerning the correctness of the hypotheses themselves. Both hypotheses have been modified and developed in the years since they were first propounded, so that only the most recent statements (Steward and Millar, 1954; Steward and Sutcliffe, 1959; Lundegårdh, 1954 and 1955) should be accepted. Earlier publications remain important for the experimental results which are contained within these papers.

Steward and his co-workers use discs of potato tuber for their experiments. The discs are prepared by washing in running tap water or changes of distilled water. The tissue reaches a relatively stable ability to absorb salt after periods of washing of the order of 24 to 48 hours at room temperature, when a respiration rate is established which remains approximately constant for long periods of time. The respiration rate of the discs is determined by the oxygen concentration of the external medium—dropping to a value about a third of that in air in zero oxygen concentration. Bromide accumulation occurs as if it is determined by aerobic processes. There is no uptake at zero oxygen tension. The uptake of potassium seems to be similarly determined, with the added complication that, at low oxygen tension, the tissue can not completely retain the ions already stored in the cells. The thickness of the discs is important in determining the rate of ion absorption and also metabolism. If the respiration rate is studied as a function of the surface area of the disc, it is found that respiration rate per specific surface (cm.^{2} per g. fresh weight) increases with increasing specific surface. Conversely, respiration per relative surface falls off with relative surface. It has been concluded that the more superficial cells contribute to a greater extent than the bulk cells to the respiration rate. Studying rubidium uptake and bromide uptake from the same point of view, it is found that, superimposed upon a uniform uptake of rubidium throughout the disc (presumably uptake into the free space), there is a marked accumulation of both rubidium and bromide in the superficial cells which is absent from the middle of a thick disc.

Discs cut from potato tubers which can accumulate bromide are also able in some degree to undergo regeneration at a cut surface in moist air. Berry and Steward (1934) found that, despite very varying responses in respiration, the ability to accumulate the bromide ion consistently implies the presence of some cells which have the ability to grow again, as shown by some degree of regeneration at a tissue surface exposed to moist air. Steward and Sutcliffe (1959) summarise the significance of this observation. They point out that the renewed ability of storage tissues to accumulate is associated with cells which have the metabolism characteristic of cells that can grow again, as best shown by their ultimate ability to divide at a cut surface. They lay stress on the point that the relationship only indicates the kind of metabolism of which the cells are capable, it does not mean that all the cells which accumulate are in the dividing state. The regeneration of cut surfaces indicates the propensity for growth and consequently it indicates the metabolic capacity of the cells.

The most significant metabolic changes which do occur in washed discs of potato are the conversion of starch to sugar in excess of that broken down by respiration and the synthesis of protein from soluble nitrogen compounds. The organic acid content of the tissue also decreases. Added salts can modify these metabolic changes. Potassium causes an increase in the rate of respiration, accompanied by increased rate of sugar breakdown. Protein synthesis is also increased. On the other hand, calcium causes a reduction in all these processes compared with the rates observed in discs remaining in distilled water.

Salt accumulation in potato discs appears to be associated with a certain metabolic state which in turn is associated with the ability of the cells to grow. The metabolism creates the overall condition in the cell which renders it capable of salt accumulation. This indicates the development of a metabolic state which allows energy to be used for salt accumulation rather than the development of a specific salt-absorbing process. Steward and Sutcliffe state, 'To understand salt accumulation in this system (washed potato discs) it is therefore necessary to visualise how energy can be donated, simultaneously to protein synthesis and to salt accumulation and how this energy could emerge from a part of the respiration which bears characteristic relations to salts and to oxygen.'

The first observations on respiration and anion uptake were made by Lundegårdh together with Burström in 1933 using intact wheat seedlings. Their results showed that, when anions are absorbed from the external solution, there is an increase in the respiration rate of the tissue above that existing when the tissue is in distilled water. Lundegårdh and Burström showed that this increase is directly related to the quantity of ions absorbed. The respiration of the tissue can therefore be divided into two components: the ground respiration unconnected with salt uptake and the respiration which is associated with the absorption of anions. No direct effect on respiration could be attributed to the uptake of cations. The term 'anion respiration' has been given to the component of respiration relating to the presence of salt in the external solution. Potassium cyanide inhibits salt accumulation and total carbon dioxide evolution (Lundegårdh and Burström, 1935). At appropriate concentrations of cyanide, the ground respiration is not affected but the anion respiration is inhibited.

Lundegårdh (1940) envisaged the following scheme to account for these findings. An oxidation-reduction potential exists across the cell membrane, depending on the oxygen gradient between the external medium and the interior of the cell. This oxidation-reduction potential is accompanied by loss of electrons from the members of the redox system. Presentation of ions to the surface of the cell results in the anions becoming combined with the members of the redox system, such that these move into the cell passing from component to component of the redox system. Correspondingly, there is a wave of electrons passing in the reverse direction to the outer surface, where the positive changes in the redox system are eliminated by reacceptance of electrons. The elements of the redox system were tentatively identified on the basis of the cyanide sensitivity of the system as haem iron in the shape of cyto-chromes. Cations were conceived to enter by direct combination with hypothetical negatively charged regions in the protoplasm and were supposed to move along 'absorption tracks' across the membrane. This cation movement is balanced by an outward movement of hydrogen ions.

Lundegårdh (1951) confirmed the presence of cytochromes in wheat roots. From spectrophotometric measurements, he showed that there is a concomitant decrease in salt absorption and of cytochrome activity in the presence of potassium cyanide in the external medium.

The phenomenon of anion respiration was shown to be observable in other tissues. Robertson (1941) showed for carrot tissue that the amount of potassium chloride absorbed is proportional to the extra carbon dioxide produced when the salt is present in the external medium. However, it was clear that, whereas the addition of an electrolyte to the external solution in-creases the respiration, this increased respiration is maintained for a considerable time in spite of the fact that the rate of accumulation falls off during this period. It did not appear from the results that the respiration rate runs parallel to the number of ions entering. Robertson and Turner (1945) showed that the salt respiration* of carrot discs is sensitive to cyanide, whereas the ground respiration is unaffected. They pointed out that these data need not demand two separate pathways of respiration, and it is quite conceivable that the cytochrome system is operating in the presence or absence of salt, being sensitive to cyanide only when operating at higher rates. In this respect it is interesting to note that Robertson, Turner and Wilkins (1947) found that, while the salt respiration of beet tissue is completely sensitive to cyanide, part of the respiration in distilled water also shows cyanide sensitivity. Robertson, Wilkins and Weeks (1951) followed up these studies with an investigation of the effect of 2:4-dinitrophenol (DNP) on salt absorption and salt-induced respiration of carrot tissue. These authors showed that, while DNP could stimulate both the ground respiration and the salt-induced respiration, salt absorption is inhibited. It was also shown that this stimulated respiration is cyanide sensitive.

This latter observation has been explained in two ways. According to Lundegårdh (1954 and 1955), only part of the cytochrome system is associated with anion uptake, namely cytochrome b. It is suggested that only cytochrome b is inhibited by DNP, and that, in the presence of DNP, electrons are transferred to molecular oxygen via the remaining cytochromes. This respiration is also cyanide sensitive. On the other hand, Robertson (1956) favours an explanation based on the structural organisation of mitochondria. Mitochondria are postulated to be primarily associated with the accumulation of ions in plant cells (Robertson, Wilkins, Hope and Nestel, 1955). DNP, by uncoupling oxidative phosphorylation prevents the transfer of phosphate, causing the mitochondria to leak and prevents them being ion accumulators—phosphorylation having an indirect effect on mitochondrial organisation.

The hypotheses which have been put forward to explain these facts have been criticised on several occasions. Nevertheless, whether or not either of the hypotheses is correct, the facts on which they are based must be considered whenever the relationship between salt absorption and metabolism is being discussed. Even if the hypotheses built on the above facts are

---

* This term was first used by Robertson (1940). It now seems certain that the observed increases in respiration are associated with the uptake of both cations and anions.

incorrect, the important observation of salt respiration still requires elucidation. It is therefore profitable to consider in more detail the exact relationship between salt respiration and the metabolism of the plant cell. For this, the work of Harley and his co-workers provides the most detailed analysis.

Unfortunately this latter work has been neglected by the majority of plant physiologists. Undoubtedly the major reason is the use of beech mycorrhizal roots in these studies. One might assume that, since this is a two-component system of fungus and angiosperm root, the system is too complicated to be considered as a physiological entity. These doubts would be well founded, if in fact there was evidence that the fungal tissue is markedly different in its physiology from the host root. On the contrary, Harley and his co-workers have taken pains to show that the two tissues are physiologically very alike. The oxygen uptake and the phosphate uptake over a range of oxygen concentrations are similar for both fungal sheath and host roots (Harley, McCready, Brierley and Jennings, 1956). Harley, McCready and Brierley (1958) showed the close parallel between the absorption and the paths of movement of phosphate within mycorrhizal roots and the events postulated by Broyer (1950) to describe the movement of bromide into barley roots. They concluded that mycorrhizal roots, although composed of two diverse organisms, have much in common with non-mycorrhizal roots and function as integrated absorbing organs. Finally, in spite of the difficulties encountered in separating the fungal sheath from the host root, there is no reason to doubt that both tissues, fungal and host, respond to the application of a suitable concentration of salt in the same manner (Harley, McCready and Geddes, 1954). The phenomenon of salt respiration is therefore a property not only of whole mycorrhizal root tips but also of each of their two tissues. Considering the vogue for comparative physiology and biochemistry, it seems strange that the component tissues, the above factual evidence apart, should not be accepted as being physiologically similar, and therefore that the whole organ should not be accepted as a single entity for most physiological studies. Many conclusions about physiological mechanisms in plant tissues have been made with knowledge drawn from studies on animal tissues. In many cases this is justifiable, but this makes the case for treating mycorrhizal roots as single functional units a still more realistic proposition, since the assumptions underlying the conclusions about higher plant physiology drawn from our knowledge of fungal physiology and vice versa must be far fewer than those underlying the conclusions drawn from animal physiology.

The respiration of freshly collected mycorrhizal roots is usually little affected by the presence of salts in the external medium, but, when such roots have been kept for a few days in aerated distilled water, they show a respiratory response to salts (Harley, McCready and Geddes, 1954). The responses to the application of phosphate and ammonium salts are the most marked. Other salts are less active in stimulating respiration. The magnitude of the response is always dependent upon the concentration of the salt over a very wide range. Owing to the fact that a quantity of information had previously been obtained concerning the absorption of phosphate by beech mycorrhizal roots (see Chapter 9), studies on salt respiration were concerned with the respiratory response to potassium dihydrogen phosphate. There is no evidence that other salts act in a dissimilar manner. It was found that the development of the property of responding to phosphate is not associated with the loss of the ion from the tissue but depends upon some temperature-sensitive reaction which occurs in the tissues during storage. The development of a respiratory response is associated with a decline in the respiratory rate of the roots in distilled water. The maximum response is not associated with carbohydrate exhaustion. This was shown to be the case from direct analysis of the carbohydrate content of roots stored for varying periods in distilled water (Jennings, 1956). Moreover, although the respiratory quotient (R.Q.) of the roots falls during storage in distilled water, there is a rise immediately upon application of salts, often to values around unity. The availability of carbohydrates in the cell to respiratory processes appears to diminish during storage; the application of salts on the other hand appears to reverse this trend, increasing the availability of carbohydrates for respiratory breakdown.

The implication of these observations becomes very much clearer when considered in conjunction with the observed relationship between oxygen consumption and phosphate absorption (Harley, McCready, Brierley and Jennings, 1956).

The phosphate uptake of freshly excised beech mycorrhizal roots, when sufficiently high concentrations of phosphate are presented, appears to be directly correlated with oxygen consumption over a wide range of oxygen concentrations. At lower concentrations of phosphate, uptake becomes increasingly independent of the external oxygen concentration above 1 per cent., indicating that phosphate absorption by the beech roots is linked with respiration but not directly linked with oxygen absorption. Certain inhibitors can inhibit phosphate absorption, while at the same time increasing oxygen uptake. DNP and sodium azide act in this manner. Carbon dioxide production, oxygen uptake and R.Q. are increased by these two inhibitors. On the other hand, phosphate uptake is reduced by those concentrations which stimulate the rise in respiration. Such effects are observed in freshly excised roots. However, when the same inhibitors are presented to roots which have been stored in distilled water the stimulated respiration is larger in proportion than similar stimulation in fresh roots.

The action of DNP is essentially an uncoupling of oxidative phosphorylation at the electron oxygen transfer level, releasing 'high-energy' phosphate acceptors* with a concomitant increase in respiration. Jennings (1958) has provided evidence that sodium azide acts in a similar manner to DNP. The increase in the stimulatory effect of these inhibitors with storage of the roots in distilled water indicates that the dependence of the respiratory rate upon high-energy phosphate acceptors increases during storage. This clearly explains the fall in the respiratory rate during this period. For, during the period in distilled water, energy-demanding processes such as synthesis or absorption might be expected to diminish, so that the availability of high-energy phosphate acceptors, which are generated in these processes, will gradually fall. This will be accompanied by a fall in the respiration rate, even though respiratory substrate in the

---

* 'High-energy' phosphate bond is something of a misnomer. Nevertheless, this term is usefully descriptive of those compounds whose phosphate bonds show a considerable standard free energy of hydrolysis. The type species, so to speak, of the genus is adenosine triphosphate (ATP) whose terminal two-phosphate bonds each yield on hydrolysis about 8000 calories per mole of free energy. Adenosine diphosphate (ADP), which in the presence of the appropriate enzymes under suitable conditions can be converted to ATP, can be considered as a 'high-energy' phosphate acceptor.

form of carbohydrate can be shown to be present. The application of any factor which stimulates the utilisation of high-energy phosphate compounds increases the supply of their precursors, and this will be reflected in an increased respiratory rate. It is significant in this respect that, when phosphate is supplied to roots stored in distilled water, the extra oxygen consumed is dependent on the concentration of phosphate. During a short period after phosphate application, the phosphate uptake and extra oxygen consumed are directly proportional. Obviously uncoupling agents such as DNP and sodium axide will cause great stimulation. Ions metabolised by the tissue, as for example ammonium and phosphate ions, will also be very effective. Ions absorbed by active transport, as might be the case for potassium, are also likely to cause an effect.

Harley and Jennings (1958) produced confirmation of this hypothesis with their study of the effect of sugars on the respiratory response to salts. Glucose, fructose or sucrose at 28 mM concentration, while maintaining the respiration of roots at a level markedly higher than equivalent samples in distilled water, prevent the respiratory response to 64 mM phosphate shown by those roots in distilled water. On the other hand, if roots which have been so treated with sugars are transferred to distilled water, with increasing duration in the latter environment, such roots begin to show a respiratory response to phosphate very much greater than those stored continuously in distilled water. Roots stored in sucrose show this large response very much earlier than those roots stored in glucose. The carbohydrate changes within the roots brought about by sugar feeding are such that it is reasonable to conclude that absorption of the sugars and the subsequent synthetic reactions involve high-energy phosphate compounds. Consequently, it is possible to account for the maintenance of a high rate of respiration and the decreased respiratory response to phosphate. Removal of the sugar from the external medium places roots under the same physiological conditions as roots kept continuously in distilled water, hence the development of an ability to show a respiratory response to phosphate. The large quantity of respiratory substrate within the roots would account for the increases over the response shown by roots kept in distilled water; while the slower rate of sucrose absorption, and the subsequent smaller quantities of carbohydrate synthesised, explain why roots fed with this sugar show this increased response in the régime in distilled water at an earlier time after the transferrence from sugar than roots fed with glucose.

Chance and Williams (1956) give a similar explanation for the anion respiration observed by Lundegårdh to that given by Harley *et al.* (1956) for their observations of the salt respiration exhibited by beech mycorrhizal roots. The spectroscopic data for wheat roots given by Lundegårdh (1954) is in good agreement with the observations on mitochondria and yeast cells made by Chance and Williams, which led them to conclude that ADP is a rate-controlling intermediate in the respiratory metabolism of baker's yeast cells. Furthermore, the anion respiration as observed by Lundegårdh and the salt respiration observed by Harley *et al.* are strictly comparable, for the observations on anion respiration were made with wheat roots stored in distilled water for 24 hours, ostensibly to bring them into a condition of low-salt status (Lundegårdh and Burström 1933b). Robertson, Turner and Wilkins (1947) observed salt respiration with beet tissue at a period when the basal respiration was known to be falling. This explanation offers a more satisfactory explanation of the observation of Robertson (1941) that salt respiration rate does not run parallel to the number of ions entering the tissue, and also those observations of Robertson, Wilkins and Weeks (1951) on the effect of DNP on carrot tissue.

There are a number of important consequences of this hypothesis. First, it is clear that high energy phosphate compounds must be closely involved in salt absorption. General considerations of ion absorption and accumulation in a variety of animal and plant cells and tissues have led to the postulation that ATP or similar compounds may be concerned in the transport of ions into the interior of the living cell. Direct evidence for this postulate is lacking for the great majority of cases, but a strong corpus of evidence is being accumulated for the direct involvement of high-energy phosphate compounds, among which ATP appears to play a key role, in the coupled movements of potassium and sodium in nerve cells and erythrocytes (see Chapter 6 for a description of the movements concerned).

The actual evidence can be summarised as follows. The

transport phenomena concerned is the coupled extrusion of sodium from the cells and the entry of potassium into the cells. Cyanide inhibits the sodium extrusion from nerve cells, and Caldwell and Keynes (1957) found that ATP injected into the axoplasm of nerves, poisoned with cyanide, partially restores the sodium efflux. Boiled ATP has no effect. Similar results have been found using erythrocyte 'ghosts', those cells which have been lysed and have lost most of their haemoglobin and a variety of other compounds, including co-enzymes and sub-strates, by exposure to hypotonic solutions. Such ghosts are able, under certain conditions, to accumulate potassium when returned to normal shape in isotonic solution. Because of this and in consequence of their permeability to hypotonic solutions, it is possible to vary the content of co-factors and substrates, making the ghosts excellent material for the study of the relationship between metabolism and ion transport. Gárdos (1954) demonstrated that, if suitable quantities of ATP are introduced into the cells during the permeable period, the cells accumulate potassium in the absence of substrate.

More direct evidence for this linkage through ATP of meta-bolism and the various ion fluxes comes from those studies on adenosine triphosphatases isolated in the membrane fraction of nerve cells and from the membranes of red cell ghosts (Skou, 1957 and 1960; Post, Merritt, Kinsolving and Albright, 1960; Dunham and Glynn, 1961; Jarnefelt, 1961). It has been shown that these phosphatases possess a marked affinity (measured by their ability to release inorganic phosphate from ATP) for potassium and sodium, as would be appropriate if the function of the enzyme were to control the magnitude of and the ratio between the intracellular potassium and sodium concentrations. The identification of these enzymes with the respective trans-port systems is confirmed by the inhibition of both enzyme activity and ion movements by cardiac glycosides such as scillaren and strophanthin G and K. These compounds do not affect the intermediary metabolism of the cell (Schatzmann, 1953), nor do they act on the energy supply to the transport mechanism (Glynn, 1957). The inhibition is quantitatively similar, half maximal activity in the presence of the inhibitor being the same for both enzyme activity and the rate of move-ment of the ions. In the cell, the adenosine triphosphatase presumably can be considered as the ion carrier, the energy for the forced movements of the ions coming from the ATP which becomes associated with the enzyme.

It has already been emphasised that the rate of respiration of a cell may be governed by the cellular concentration of high-energy phosphate acceptors, which in turn is determined by the activity of the various mechanisms causing hydrolysis of the high-energy phosphate compounds, such as ATP. As one such mechanism could be active transport, it is of great interest that it is possible to bring about an inhibition of potassium accumu-lation with cardiac glycosides, and that this inhibition is accompanied by a drop in the rate of respiration. Whittam (1961) has shown that this can happen with brain slices treated with strophanthin G (ouabain). This compound at $5 \mu M$ concentration causes both a fall of 70 per cent. in the potassium concentration of the cells and a 50 per cent. drop in their rate of oxygen uptake. Replacement of sodium in the medium by choline causes a similar drop in oxygen uptake of the cells. Under these latter circumstances, strophanthin G causes no further fall. The parallelism of the effects of strophanthin G and sodium on the maintenance of the tissue-potassium con-centration and on the rate of oxygen uptake suggests that the active transport of cations may control the rate of at least half the respiratory activity of brain tissue. This control of the rate of respiration by the transport of ions is entirely analogous to salt respiration observed with plant tissues, though it is apparent, from what has been described for potassium-sodium movements in erythrocytes and nerve cells, that a specific high-energy phosphate (in this case ATP) can be implicated with some certainty as a key factor in the control mechanism in the erythrocytes.

Even if the actual high-energy phosphate compounds involved in solute transport can be identified, the actual characterisation of the situation where the high-energy phos-phate compound is having its influence will depend upon a much fuller knowledge of the various structural features of the system involved. Mitchell (1959) has pointed out the necessity of taking such structural features into account and has suggested a mechanism for the transport of phosphate into cells of *Staphy-lococcus aureus* in which the stoichiometry of the system plays an important part. The ions are transported by a mechanism driven by metabolism, presumably involving ATP, in a unidirectional manner, except when respiration is minimal. In these latter circumstances, exchange of phosphate occurs between the cell and the external medium.

In view of the above discussion, it might be profitable to examine the possibility of an explanation involving high-energy phosphate compounds for the observations of Steward and his co-workers. All storage tissues show an increased respiration after cutting. MacDonald and De Kock (1958) have demonstrated this phenomenon for discs of carrot, potato, red beet, sugar beet and swede tissue. The rate of respiration rises for at least three to four days after cutting the discs, the rate of increase depending on the temperature of incubation (the three to four days is a minimum period for all the tissues studied at an incubation temperature of 25°). While the respiration rate may vary after this period, frequently declining, the initial increase is always associated with that period during which storage tissues develop an ability to absorb salts.

The increased respiration which develops as a result of cutting shows frequently a changing sensitivity to inhibitors. The most significant studies, from the point of view of this discussion, have been those in which the effect of DNP on the respiration of freshly-cut storage tissue and on that of similar tissue aged after cutting has been compared (Laties, 1959b and c; Hackett, Hass, Griffiths and Niederpruem, 1960). With both chicory root (Laties) and potato (Hackett et al.), DNP stimulates the respiration of freshly-cut tissue but has little or no effect upon the respiration of tissue aged for twenty-four hours or more. In the case of chicory root, the respiratory increase induced by DNP is little less than the maximum increment induced by ageing the tissue. On the other hand, with potato tissue, the rate of the respiration induced by ageing is twice that of the uncoupled respiration of freshly-cut tissue treated with DNP. It is clear from this difference in rate that the respiration induced by ageing cannot be due to the uncoupling of respiration. This is confirmed by the fact that essentially all the DNP-stimulated respiration of freshly-cut slices of potato is inhibited by cyanide, whereas the DNP-stimulated respiration of slices maintained in distilled water for twenty-four hours is

F

unaffected by cyanide. Similarly, although both the respiratory increment induced in fresh tissue of chicory root by DNP and the increment induced by ageing are malonate sensitive, in the former case there is no recovery with added malate following malonate inhibition, whereas in the latter case there is recovery and sometimes stimulation of the rate of respiration. With chicory root tissue one cannot be absolutely certain that the increased respiration, although involving a different pathway, is not the result of uncoupling.

If the increase in rate of respiration of potato tissue brought by ageing is not due to uncoupling, other alternative explanations must be sought. The observations of MacDonald and De Kock (1958) clearly show that there is ample respiratory substrate in the form of sugars present in potato discs during the period under discussion. Hackett *et al.* (1960), with their studies on isolated mitochondria, showed that there is no change in the ability of these particles to oxidise succinate, α-ketoglutarate or citrate when the particles are extracted from fresh or aged tissues. The phosphorylating ability also remains constant. Furthermore, although the respiratory components of the electron transport chain undergoes measurable changes, these changes can in no way account for the five times increase in rate shown by the respiration of the whole tissue.

A clue to the factors involved in the observed increase in respiration comes from some studies on the incorporation of phosphate into freshly excised and aged tissue (Loughman, 1957 and 1960; Calo, Marks and Varner, 1957; Hackett *et al.*, 1960). It has been shown that potato discs show an increasing capacity to take up phosphate from the external solution with increase in time after cutting. The changing ability of the tissue to absorb phosphate could be due to the cells becoming more permeable. However, the fact that freshly-cut potato tissue loses phosphate argues against this hypothesis. On the other hand, aged discs not only absorb greater quantities of phosphate, which is retained under those conditions in which phosphate is lost by fresh discs, but also show an increasing capacity to metabolise the phosphate once it is absorbed. The incorporation of phosphate into organic compounds increases at a rate similar to the respiration rate. Thus only 20 per cent. of the phosphate absorbed from 10^{-5} M solution during a five minute period by fresh discs is esterified, while 80 per cent. is esterified during the same period by aged discs. It is of interest that of this 80 per cent. of phosphate esterified, 30 per cent. is recovered as nucleotides. Obviously the net syntheses must be measured, but this result indicates that nucleotide synthesis may be occurring. Should this be so, then there is a basis for many of the various observations on the ageing of potato discs. Increased production of nucleotides will be important not only in their relationship to rates of respiration but also to protein synthesis and, if the ideas presented above are correct, to salt absorption.

CHAPTER 6

POTASSIUM AND SODIUM UPTAKE

Yeast

The most detailed study of the relationship between potassium and sodium ions and a plant cell has been made upon yeast. It is hoped that a consideration of the facts appertaining to such studies will throw some light on similar studies with other plant material. The situation as investigated in studies upon yeast has proved to be complicated; a similar complexity may account for the inability of various investigators using other plant material to find a simple kinetic description of the uptake of alkali cations.

In yeast, potassium ions are taken up in exchange for hydrogen ions derived from metabolic reactions (Rothstein and Enns, 1946). Conway and Brady (1950) showed that, when yeast is fermenting glucose in unbuffered solutions, organic acid appears in the medium. The organic acid so produced is mainly succinic acid. When potassium chloride is added to the medium, the rate of production of succinic acid in the medium falls while the concentration of hydrogen ions increases. It seems that succinic acid is the major source of the hydrogen ions which are exchanged for potassium, the potassium succinate being retained inside the cells. On the other hand, if cells are aerated for a considerable time before fermentation, there is a fall in the quantity of succinic acid extruded. Even so, the exchange of hydrogen for potassium reaches maximum values. It appears that, under these conditions, extra bicarbonate is formed in the cells in a concentration almost equivalent to the potassium absorbed. Both hydrogen ions and potassium move against large concentration gradients (Rothstein and Enns, 1946). The cytoplasmic concentrations of potassium and hydrogen are approximately 2×10^{-1}M and 1×10^{-6}M respectively. Yet there is uptake of potassium and excretion of hydrogen ions when the concentration of both ions in the external medium is 1×10^{-4}M. The mechanism of uptake is highly specific for potassium and strongly discriminates in favour of potassium when other alkali cations are present (Conway and Duggan, 1958) (see Table 5).

TABLE 5

The relative transport affinity of a cation for the yeast cell which was determined from the relation $(K)/(X) \times 100$, where (K) and (X) are the concentrations of potassium and the cation investigated, when the uptake of potassium is depressed by 50 per cent. Suspensions were made of 1 g. of yeast in 5 to 200 ml. depending on the cations being examined, and the suspending fluid contained 5 per cent. glucose

(Conway and Duggan, 1958)

Cation	Relative Transport Affinities
K	100
Rb	42
Cs	7
Na	3·8
Li	0·5
Mg	0·5

Conway has suggested that the hydrogen ions must be produced near the outer region of the cell, a conclusion in accord with the observations of Rothstein (1954) that the glycolytic reactions of the yeast cell are located near the cell surface.

Ordinarily yeast is rich in potassium and low in sodium. However, under certain conditions, cells become rich in sodium (Conway and Moore, 1954).

Hevesy and Nielson (1941) found that the uptake of ^{42}K is greater than the uptake of potassium measured chemically. This indicates that there is an exhange of cellular ^{39}K for ^{42}K, in addition to the net uptake of potassium. As well as this, Rothstein and Enns observed a slow leakage of potassium ion from the cell during periods of starvation, which is largely in exchange for extracellular hydrogen ion. This loss of potassium is increased during fermentation.

The most important studies of this phenomenon of potassium exchange have been made by Rothstein and Bruce (1958a and b). There are two major problems which have to be overcome in a truly quantitative study of the influx and efflux of potassium ions which comprise the exchange situation. The cells rapidly

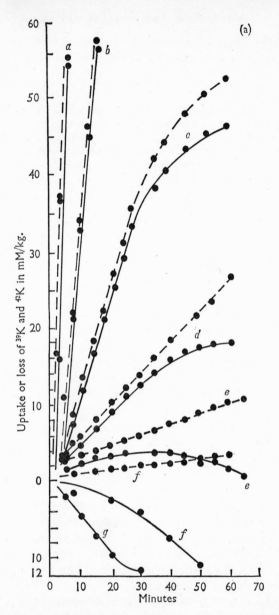

FIG. 6(a). Uptake or loss of ^{39}K and ^{42}K by fermenting yeast cells at different external concentrations of potassium using a cell-column technique. The amounts of yeast on the column were 600 mg. for potassium concentrations below 1×10^{-3}M and 1200 mg. for higher concentrations. The glucose concentration was 0.05 M and the pH 4.0.

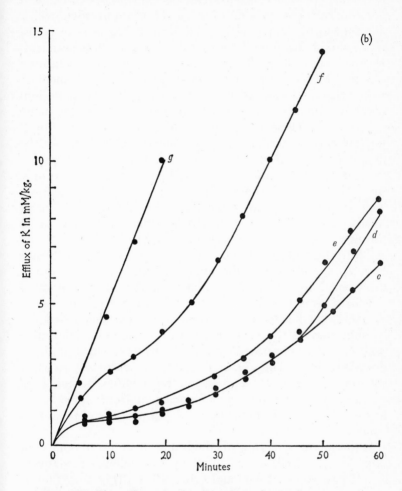

FIG. 6(b) The efflux of potassium from fermenting yeast at different external concentrations of potassium. The data are calculated from Fig. 6a by subtracting values of ^{39}K from values for ^{42}K. (a), potassium in the external solution at $1 \times 10^{-2}M$; (b) $2 \times 10^{-3}M$; (c), $1 \times 10^{-3}M$; (d), $3 \times 10^{-4}M$; (e), $1 \times 10^{-4}M$; (f), $3 \times 10^{-5}M$ and (g) no potassium in the external solution. Solid lines represent uptake or loss of ^{39}K; broken lines, ^{42}K (Rothstein and Bruce, 1958a).

alter the potassium concentration of the medium, expecially at
low concentrations, so that the rates of influx and efflux, which
are dependent upon the extracellular concentration of potassium, also change rapidly during the course of an experiment.
Determination of the fluxes requires the use of the potassium
isotope ^{42}K. Since ^{42}K has a short half-life, its specific activity
diminishes to such an extent that the chemical level of potassium
necessary for adequate counting becomes too high for many
experiments. These technical problems were overcome by a
method which permits the continuous replacement of the
medium (Rothstein and Bruce, 1958a). The medium is passed
through a short column of cells at such a rate that there are only
small changes in the potassium concentration of the medium.
This means that, as far as the external medium is concerned,
steady-state conditions are realised. The medium, having passed
through the column, is collected for analysis.

The influx of potassium ions is given by the difference
between the change in the total concentration of potassium
determined by chemical methods and the concentration of
labelled ions in the medium. Frequently, the determination of
the rate of efflux of an ion from a cell has demanded the
equilibration of the cellular ion with a suitable radioactive
isotope. This is not necessary with the method which has been
described above. The advantage can most clearly be seen when
studying the efflux into a potassium-free medium, because with
the above method the loss of potassium from the cells, as
measured by chemical means, is a direct measure of potassium
efflux.

It was found using these methods that the influx of potassium
into the yeast cell, as measured by ^{42}K, follows a relatively
simple pattern (Rothstein and Bruce, 1958a) (Fig. 6). At lower
concentrations of potassium, the influx is essentially linear with
time, but, at the higher concentrations, there is some flattening
out of the curves, which could be due to the efflux of absorbed
^{42}K. The rate of potassium influx increases in an asymptotic
manner with increasing concentrations of extracellular potassium. However, the rates of efflux in the presence of extracellular potassium are much more complicated. While in a
potassium-free medium efflux proceeds at a constant rate of
15 mM per kg. cells per hour, in the presence of extracellular

potassium the efflux is negligible for an initial period of time but then increases to a rate comparable to that for a potassium-free medium. The delay in the appearance of high rates of efflux becomes longer with higher concentrations of potassium, so that at the highest potassium concentrations the rate of efflux becomes difficult to determine.

Rothstein and Bruce (1958b) also studied the potassium efflux in the absence of extracellular potassium. The rate of efflux could be changed by the presence of various substrates. Glucose, fructose and pyruvate increase the rate of efflux. On the other hand, the efflux of potassium is reduced in the presence of lactate and ethyl alcohol. In the absence of substrate, the efflux under anaerobic conditions is reduced to a very low level, but, in the presence of substrate, the rate is unchanged by anaerobiosis. The efflux of potassium is markedly temperature sensitive. With or without glucose in the external medium, the Q_{10} for efflux is 3·0 between 5° and 15°, and 2·0 between 15° and 25°. When no substrate is present, the loss of potassium from the cell is in exchange for hydrogen ions in the medium. In the presence of glucose, this relationship is obscured by the excretion of organic acids. Below pH 4·5, sodium tends to reduce potassium efflux, though this effect depends on the concentration of sodium, for above 0·05 M sodium the rate of potassium efflux in the presence of glucose is greater than that shown by the controls. Above pH 4·5, the potassium efflux increases markedly in the presence of sodium. This is a non-specific cation effect, since triethylamine chloride is as effective as sodium chloride.

Various inhibitors produce a variety of responses. 2×10^{-3} M sodium azide increases the rate of efflux initially, but the rate of efflux falls to a low level after 45 to 60 minutes. This initial stimulation of efflux is increased by the presence of glucose. DNP at 10^{-3} M behaves like azide. At a lower concentration $(1 \times 10^{-4}$ M), the efflux is increased only in the absence of glucose. The efflux in the presence of 2×10^{-3} M cyanide is not as great as that produced by 2×10^{-3} M azide.

Dramatic effects are produced by certain dyes. Of the dyes tested (at 10^{-4} M concentration), Rothstein and Bruce found that those with a redox potential less than 0·10 mV, produce a very high rate of efflux, while those with a redox potential greater than this value have very little effect on efflux. Mercury compounds are equally effective at even lower concentrations. With the highest concentration of mecuric chloride tested, the rate is so rapid that 80 per cent. of the cellular potassium is lost in one hour. The effect of mercury salts is equally great whether or not glucose is present, and, once established, the rate of efflux can not be reversed by cysteine, although efflux is prevented if cysteine is present initially. It was later shown (Passow, Loewenstein and Rothstein, 1959; Passow and Rothstein, 1960) that both methylene blue and mercury salts act in an all-or-none manner upon the yeast cell. At any given concentration of agent, a proportion of cells lose their potassium. The cells that are affected in this manner also become permeable to dye—the number of stained cells is directly related to loss of potassium. Before methylene blue can be effective, it must first become bound to the cell. Protection can be afforded by the presence of inorganic cations—the dye forming a less stable complex with the cell than bivalent cations but a more stable complex than monovalent cations. The negative groups with which the methylene blue is associated have been identified by Passow *et al.* as phosphoryl groups, perhaps ribonucleic acid in view of the fact that treatment of yeast cells with ribonuclease reduces the binding of methylene blue (Hiaoka and Takada, 1957). Once associated with the cell, the methylene blue exerts its effect upon those groups associated with cell permeability. Mercury has a direct effect upon these latter groups.*

Rothstein and Bruce (1959b) suggested that changes in the rates of efflux observed could be attributed to (1) change in the driving force or (2) change in the resistance of a membrane barrier to cation penetration. Thus the increased potassium efflux at low pH and at high pH in the presence of sodium could be attributed to an increased activity gradient across the cell

---

* It is extremely interesting to note that surface-active agents appear to act in a similar manner upon the permeability of yeast cells (Armstrong, 1957; Scharff and Beck, 1959; Scharff and Maupin, 1960). Cationic detergents (such as bradosol and benzalkonium chloride), at suitable concentrations, inhibit fermentation and bring about the loss of potassium and phosphate from the cells. Anionic detergents, bile salts and straight-chain fatty acids have no effect. Addition of uranyl ions, in sufficient quantity to saturate the surface polyphosphate groups of the cell, prevent the inhibitory action of bradosol, while it has been shown that the effects of benzalkonium chloride can be interpreted as an all-or-none phenomenon.

membrane. In the latter situation, sodium could exchange for potassium within the cell, whereas in the former situation hydrogen ions exchange for potassium ions, since the yeast cell shows a greater affinity for hydrogen ions. Similarly, the diminished rate of potassium efflux, after the first hour of experiments, with the higher concentrations of mercuric chloride could be accounted for by the large losses of cellular potassium. This explanation can be invoked for the decrease in efflux brought about by presence of potassium in the external medium (Rothstein and Bruce, 1958a). If the loss of potassium from the cell depends on the ionic activity gradient, then external potassium will reduce the rate of efflux—the amount of reduction depending on the concentration of potassium in the external medium. On the other hand, the yeast cell will be accumulating potassium under these conditions, and, should the internal potassium concentration increase above that in the external solution, the efflux should commence.

This explanation leads one to visualise the loss of potassium ions as being governed by the 'leakiness' of the cell. If this explanation is correct, potassium ions are lost by diffusion in exchange for other cations in the external medium. The rate of diffusion will not only depend on the activity gradient between potassium within the cell and that in the medium, but also upon the resistance of any barriers to this diffusion process. Rothstein and Bruce (1958b) suggest, from the observed action of mercury salts, that sulphydryl groups may be involved in controlling the resistance of the barrier within the cell to cation penetration. Two further papers from Rothstein's laboratory have amplified this concept (Passow, Rothstein and Loewenstein, 1959; Passow and Rothstein, 1960). The experimental data suggest that the interaction of both mercury and methylene blue with a membrane site constitutes a stress. No physiological response is observed until the total stress reaches the breaking-point of the membrane. These authors suggested that methylene blue might react with the sulphydryl group forming disulphide bridges (only the oxidised form of the dye is effective in producing leakage), while mercury forms $-S-Hg-S-$ bridges. There are two difficulties with this concept. First, as pointed out by Passow and Rothstein, leakage shows a high degree of specificity with regard to heavy metals. Mercury, copper, lead and zinc ions can all react with sulphydryl groups, yet only mercury and copper ions can produce leakage of potassium from the yeast cell. Presumably there are other factors relating to the exact location of the sulphydryl groups which determines their interaction with the various metal ions. The second difficulty is concerned with the relation of the effects observed with mercury and methylene blue to the efflux observed under more normal metabolic conditions. The action of both mercury and methylene blue is irreversible. Furthermore the permeability of the cell in the presence of mercury differs from that of untreated cells. With mercury, the cell becomes permeable to both cations and anions (Passow and Rothstein, 1960). Orthophosphate and manganous ions can move freely to and from the yeast cell under these conditions, whereas yeast cells in the absence of any fermentable substrate are markedly impermeable to these ions. The efflux of potassium under more normal conditions cannot be due to breakdown of the membrane. Any relationship between potassium efflux and sulphydryl groups in the normal cell will obviously be more subtle than that observed between the increase in the permeability of the cell and mercury poisoning.

Rothstein and Bruce (1958b) suggested that oxygen, temperature, azide, cyanide, DNP and substrates, in producing varying rates of potassium efflux according to the conditions in the external medium, may be acting on the sulphydryl groups in an indirect manner by altering the redox potential at the surface of the cell. It is certain that there is some connection between the redox potential and metabolism, for the potential established by yeast and the surrounding medium is shifted markedly by the addition of glucose (Conway and Kernan, 1955). Rothstein and Bruce point out that this explanation by no means covers the facts, for azide and cyanide, by blocking the cytochrome system, reduce the yeast cell to the anaerobic mode of metabolism. However, whereas these agents increase the rate of efflux, anaerobiosis decreases the rate. In view of the discussion in the previous paragraph, it might be wise to keep in mind the possibility of alternative explanations for the phenomenon of potassium efflux.

The only other study specifically devoted to the loss of potassium from plant tissues has been made by Harley and

Wilson (1959) using beech mycorrhizal roots. They showed that the loss of potassium from such roots is markedly temperature dependent. At temperatures below 20°, it is not always possible to detect potassium loss in the time intervals used to study the phenomenon. Anaerobic conditions, sodium azide, DNP and iodo-acetate all bring about a significant loss of potassium from the tissue. The experimental conditions do not allow any discrimination between the processes of influx and efflux. The observed losses of potassium could be caused by decreases in the rate of influx.

Conway, Ryan and Carton (1954) observed that yeasts, which have a considerable fraction of their internal potassium replaced by sodium, lose sodium ions into distilled water. The loss of sodium ions is accompanied by bicarbonate ions and organic acid cations. Foulkes (1956) also made a study of sodium loss from sodium-rich yeast, though it was less detailed than that made by Conway $et\ al$. The two sets of data differ with respect to the observed effects of metabolic inhibitors. Conway $et\ al$. observed that azide and DNP (both at 2×10^{-3} M) have no effect on the loss of sodium into distilled water. Cyanide and anaerobic conditions reduce sodium loss to zero. Foulkes did not confirm these observations. He found that azide increases the rate of sodium loss above the control values and that in fact, in all conditions in which the rate of oxygen uptake is reduced, sodium loss consistently exceeds the control values. Foulkes suggested that such differences in experimental observations may be a reflection of the intercellular concentration of sodium and potassium.

Neither Conway $et\ al$. nor Foulkes made their studies on the sodium loss from yeast under steady state conditions. A comparison between these results and the data concerning potassium fluxes obtained by Rothstein and Bruce must be made with caution. It is possible that sodium loss from sodium-rich yeast observed by Conway $et\ al$. is mediated by the same process as that governing potassium efflux. Significantly both processes are inhibited by cyanide and anaerobic conditions (it must be emphasised at this point that this comparison must be made for those conditions in which there is no external fermentable substrate). Conway and Kernan (1955) found that, when the redox potential of a yeast suspension is lowered by certain redox dyes, the rate of loss of sodium is increased over that of the control value. The dyes which produce this effect are the same as those which increase the rate of efflux of potassium from normal yeast cells and which Conway and Kernan found would decrease the rate of potassium uptake below the control values.

Two pieces of evidence are against this supposition that potassium efflux and sodium loss are mediated by the same mechanism. First azide has no effect on sodium loss from sodium-rich yeast but increases potassium efflux. Possible explanations lie in the different conditions used. It may be significant that potassium efflux observed in the presence of azide returned to a low level after 45 to 60 minutes. On the other hand, there is a striking difference in the reaction to heavy metals. Mention has been made of the high rates of potassium efflux in the presence of mercury salts. In complete contrast, mercury salts (in fact a variety of salts of heavy metals have the same effect) completely inhibit sodium loss. One might conclude from this that the groups which are sensitive to mercury in the yeast used by Rothstein are protected in some way in the yeast used by Conway. This however would only explain any lack of stimulation of sodium loss. Alternatively this hypothesis may be wrong. Other hypotheses are possible with the data as they stand. For instance, it is possible that the redox dyes have no effect on sodium loss in Conway and Kernan's experiments but are preventing sodium from being reaccumulated by the yeast cell. It would be wiser to await an examination of the separate effects of inhibitors on sodium efflux and influx before any definite conclusion is drawn. Exactly the same proviso stands for the effects of various inhibitors on potassium efflux observed by Rothstein and Bruce (1958b). These data cannot provide any complete interpretation of the inhibitor studies on net uptake until further investigations have been made on the relationship between potassium influx and added inhibitors.

Algae

Algae which grow in the sea or brackish water (where there is also a high content of sodium and a low concentration of potassium in the medium) show a striking capacity to regulate the potassium and sodium content of their cells. Thus Eppley

(1958a) has shown, from analyses of tissues which had been growing in the sea, that sodium is excluded from the cells of *Porphyra perforata* by a factor of ten, while potassium is accumulated to a concentration some forty times that of sea water.

There have been two methods of approach to the study of potassium and sodium movements in algal cells. One approach is the same as that for studies on the net fluxes in yeast cells and is concerned with their relationship to metabolism within the cell. Other studies have been concerned with the individual fluxes of potassium and sodium between vacuoles of coenocytic algae and the external medium. The measurement of potential differences between the vacuole and the external medium is closely connected with these latter studies, for interpretation of data obtained by one method depends on the data obtained using the other. Such studies have been discussed in Chapter 3. An important finding from such studies is the fact that in *Nitellopsis* and *Halicystis* it appears that potassium moves passively into the cell, whereas sodium is pumped out of the cell.

In algae, the situation is often complicated by the effect of light. Roberts, Roberts and Cowie (1949) found that the uptake of potassium by *Chlamydomonas humicolor* is stimulated by light. On the other hand, glucose in the medium will stimulate uptake in the dark. Scott and Hayward (1953a) found that, when *Ulva* is transferred from light to dark, potassium is lost from the cells, while the sodium content of the cells increases. Scott and Ericson (1955) found a similar relationship between illumination and cobalt absorption by *Rhodymenia palmata*. Radioactive cobalt absorbed whilst the thallus is illuminated is subsequently lost in the dark. The effect of light appears to be due to alterations of carbon dioxide concentrations within the thallus. Eppley (1958a) found that, when tissues of *Porphyra perforata* are kept in light or dark for seventeen days, there is no difference in potassium or sodium contents of the cells as the result of the two treatments.* However, light is not without its effect upon the potassium-sodium balance within the cells, for, following exposure to anoxia, potassium accumulation and

* The task of estimating cellular ion concentration in *Porphyra* is complicated by the large number of cation binding sites on extracellular material (probably galactan sulphate). Tissues which have been in sea water may contain as much as 40 m. equiv. sodium per kg. fresh weight and 10 mM calcium per kg. fresh weight associated with this extracellular material.

sodium extrusion take place and the two processes are accelerated by light. Five per cent. carbon dioxide-air completely inhibits the recovery from anoxia in the dark, suggesting that the effect of light is through the reduction of the carbon dioxide concentration within the cells. While this may be so, light may have a more direct effect upon the ionic balance of cells as a result of energy being supplied to transport processes via photosynthesis.

Iodoacetate (10^{-3} M) induces potassium loss from both *Porphyra* and *Ulva*. In both cases, this inhibitory effect is removed by light. It is also significant that iodoacetate (10^{-2} M) completely inhibits the net uptake of potassium by yeast cells (Conway and O'Malley, 1946). However, *Porphyra* and *Ulva* are not completely identical in their reaction to iodoacetate. In the presence of iodoacetate, there is a marked uptake of sodium by *Ulva*, but iodoacetate has no effect on the sodium balance of *Porphyra*. Scott and Hayward (1953a and 1954) analysed in some detail the effect of iodoacetate on potassium uptake and sodium extrusion in *Ulva*. In the first instance, they showed that iodoacetate penetrates the tissue in light, which emphasises that there must be some fairly direct action of light on potassium and sodium movements. 5×10^{-3} M sodium arsenate completely prevents any potassium loss in the presence of iodoacetate in the dark, but has no effect on sodium uptake caused by the latter inhibitor. There is a parallel with yeast, for Hayward (1954) observed that arsenate offers complete protection against the loss of potassium observed in the presence of iodoacetate under aerobic conditions, though here there is also protection against sodium gain. Phosphoglycerate in the presence of iodoacetate allows significant but not complete protection against potassium loss from *Ulva* but has no effect upon sodium gain. On the other hand, phenylurethane, when added with iodoacetate in the light, causes loss of potassium and gain of sodium, shifts which are very much greater than those observed with phenylurethane alone. Finally, whereas pyruvate (50 mg. per cent.) offers no protection against the loss of potassium caused by iodoacetate in the dark, sodium gain under the same circumstances is completely inhibited. Dinitrocresol ($3\cdot3 \times 10^{-5}$ M) in the dark produces a loss of potassium and a gain of sodium, there being very much greater movements of sodium than potassium.

Scott and Hayward (1955) suggest that potassium movement into and sodium movement out of *Ulva* cells are controlled by metabolic reactions within the cell. It is suggested that potassium movement out of *Ulva* cells and sodium movement in the reverse direction is by diffusion along a concentration gradient. From their inhibitor studies, Scott and Hayward suggest that potassium uptake is connected with the metabolic sequences associated with the breakdown of phosphoglyceric acid, while sodium loss from the cells is much more closely connected with the photochemical reaction of photosynthesis. It is suggested that the effect of light on potassium retention is a result of photosynthetic production of phosphoglyceric acid, and iodo-acetate exerts its effect on the production of phosphoglyceric acid from 3-phosphoglyceraldehyde by interference with the sulphydryl groups of phosphoglyceraldehyde dehydrogenase. It is possible that sulphydryl groups are also associated with sodium extrusion, though their metabolic location is different from those which are responsible for potassium retention, since arsenate shows no protective effect on sodium uptake caused by iodoacetate. Such a hypothesis demands much further work before it can provide a satisfactory explanation of the potassium and sodium fluxes in *Ulva*. The action of several of the inhibitors used in the experiments described above is too unspecific to provide any detailed information. The loss of potassium and uptake of sodium from *Ulva* cells in the presence of phenylurethane in the light must be due to other causes than the cessation of photosynthesis, for the rates of flux are totally different from those in the dark, when photosynthesis had also ceased.

However, these results can be criticised at a much more fundamental level. All the measurements so far described have been made upon net fluxes. The only valid data for any decision about the mechanisms responsible for the movement of an ion into and out of a cell must be based upon measurements of the actual individual fluxes. The above study can, in actual fact, only be considered as an investigation into the metabolic factors regulating the *levels* of potassium and sodium within the cells of *Ulva*.

It has been hinted that there may be similarities between the cells of algae and yeast in the manner in which their potassium

G

and sodium balance is maintained. Whether this will prove to be so will depend on further work. Scott and Hayward (1953b) showed that the rate of potassium exchange in illuminated *Ulva* cells is not too different from that of strongly fermenting yeast (Hevesy and Nielson, 1941). This fact together with the results obtained with iodoacetate suggests that the mechanism responsible for potassium balance may be similar in the two organisms. Nevertheless, there are distinctive features about the permeability properties of the marine algae in comparison with yeast. Both Scott and Hayward (1954) and Eppley (1958a) found with *Ulva* and *Porphyra* respectively that both potassium and sodium are lost from tissues when they are placed in 0·6 M sucrose. In *Ulva*, 85 per cent. of the two ions are lost within 2 to 3 hours. In *Porphyra*, sodium loss is found to be rapid; after a few hours the sodium remaining in the tissues becomes constant —a value which is independent of whether the tissue is dead or alive. The rate of exchange of radioactive sodium between the cells of *Ulva* and the external medium, when compared with other tissues, is extremely fast (Scott, de Voe, Hayward and Craven, 1957). Within 5 seconds, 80 per cent. of the sodium inside the tissue exchanges with sodium in the external medium. The rate of exchange is independent of temperature, except for a small fraction which exchanges at a slower rate at 1° compared with the rate at 20°. Neither phenylurethane nor uranyl ions interfere with the incorporation of radioactive sodium preparatory to exchange experiments. The temperature independence suggests a purely physical process of exchange, though the lack of inhibition with uranyl ion nullifies any idea that the exchange is solely into a Donnan space equivalent to that found in higher plants. The whole cytoplasm of these algae appears to be extremely permeable to sodium ions. Potassium exchange, on the other hand, appears to be metabolically determined—the rate of exchange increasing with temperature between 20° and 30° (Scott and Hayward, 1953b). Light brings about a further increase in the rate of exchange at both temperatures.

The very striking permeability features turn attention away from inhibitor studies and focus it upon those changes in the potassium and sodium content of these algae which are brought about by concentration changes in the external medium. Of the two algal species, the most detailed information has been provided by Eppley (1958a and b, 1959) for *Porphyra*. Transference of discs of tissue of this alga to potassium-free artificial sea water causes a loss of potassium and a gain of sodium within the cells. These changes are not attributable to any inhibition of metabolism as measured by oxygen consumption. On adding potassium chloride or rubidium chloride to the medium, net accumulation of potassium or rubidium takes place, which is accompanied by net extrusion of sodium ions. The rates of potassium or rubidium accumulation and sodium extrusion are proportional to the amount of potassium chloride or rubidium chloride which is added only at the lower concentrations. Saturation of rates is evident at potassium or rubidium concentrations above 20 to 30 m.equiv.

It is impossible to say whether potassium accumulation and sodium extrusion are coupled in any way since only net fluxes have been determined. The remarks concerning the data for *Ulva* apply equally to that for *Porphyra*, and it is again pointed out that measurement of individual fluxes is necessary before any decision can be made on this point. Nevertheless, it is interesting that the potassium and sodium content of the cells show no stoichiometric relationship. For instance, net potassium accumulation continues after net sodium extrusion has ceased and net potassium loss in potassium-free sea water continues after the net sodium gain is complete. The data obtained with iodoacetate also illustrate this. Finally, when the sodium level of the cells is reduced as a result of placing the tissues in lithium-sea water (both potassium and sodium ions replaced by lithium ions), potassium accumulation will still take place when potassium chloride is added to the medium, even though there is only a low level of sodium within the cells.

In view of the marked permeability of the cells to cations, it is possible to provide a reasonably simple explanation of these findings. It can be assumed that the cytoplasm contains fixed anionic groups with which cations will become associated. Unless any individual cation is accumulated by a special mechanism, the cation retaining capacity of the tissue is limited by the number of such anionic groups. If potassium is accumulated when the tissue is low in potassium, it will displace sodium from these anionic sites, and, since the cell is very permeable to sodium ions, these ions will be displaced from the cell. When the potassium accumulation mechanism is inhibited, sodium, owing to its higher concentration in sea water, will rapidly diffuse into the cell and displace potassium. Although the concentration of a number of cations is probably governed by the number of anionic groups in the cytoplasm, potassium ions will be accumulated over and above the concentration to maintain equivalence with such groups. This explains the lack of any stoichiometric relationship between the potassium and sodium content of the cells. The fact that magnesium and lithium reduce the sodium content of the cells to a very low level yet allow potassium accumulation to proceed, as far as can be gathered, at an unimpeded rate suggests that magnesium and lithium prevent sodium from being associated with the fixed anionic groups of the cell. Epstein (1960) has pointed out the similarity between the absorption of lithium and alkaline earth absorption by barley roots. It may be concluded that lithium ions will be very much more strongly associated than other alkali ions with the anionic groups of the cell. Potassium accumulation can still proceed, the potassium which is accumulated being unassociated with the fixed anionic groups.

With this discussion in mind, it is profitable to return to the data obtained from inhibitor studies. There is every indication that the situation with regard to potassium-sodium content applies to *Ulva* as well as *Porphyra*. Metabolic inhibitors can influence the cation balance at two points. They might inhibit the potassium accumulation mechanism. Iodoacetate and phenylurethane appear to inhibit in this manner. Iodoacetate may act by destroying the metabolic coupling between respiration and the accumulating system, while phenyl urethane may act both on this coupling and the metabolic coupling between photosynthesis and the accumulating system. Dinitrocresol would presumably also act directly upon the potassium accumulation mechanism in a similar manner to iodoacetate. The increased rate of glycolysis and carbon dioxide production, which would be expected in the presence of this inhibitor, could account for the very much greater rise in the level of sodium within the cells than that observed with iodoacetate. Loss of phosphate from *Ulva* cells is known to occur in the presence of iodoacetate in the dark (at the same rate as the loss of potassium with the same concentration of inhibitor) (Scott and Hayward, 1953). Other changes in ion movements may occur, with consequent alterations of anion content.

Higher plants

The data concerning potassium and sodium movements between the cells of yeast and marine algae have been reviewed in some detail. It has been shown that the situation with regard to these two ions is complex. In any analysis of net uptake, fluxes in both directions have to be considered. Until recently, all studies of potassium and sodium movements into higher plant tissues, whether they be storage tissue or growing plant roots, have been solely concerned with net uptake. It has been customary to equate net uptake with influx of these ions. This is not permissible, and any observed change in the rate of net uptake could equally be the result of a change in the rate of either influx or efflux. Such a state of affairs will complicate any kinetic analysis. Certainly, it will invalidate any analysis of net uptake considered solely in terms of a process of influx. However, for many years it has only been possible to study net uptake. Only with the use of radioactive traders can the processes of influx and efflux be dissociated.

The loss of potassium by plant tissues has been observed many times. It is particularly striking in discs of freshly-cut storage tissue, when they are placed in distilled water (Steward, 1932; Asprey, 1937). However, when the tissues are stored for increasing periods in distilled water, the loss of potassium drops to a low level. This phenomenon has been ascribed to the damage caused by cutting, and in no way has a loss of potassium been considered as a normal physiological process.

The first demonstration that net uptake of potassium observed in storage tissue is a function of influx and efflux of the ion was made by Briggs (1957c) in an analysis of the data of Sutcliffe (1954) for potassium exchange in beet discs. Briggs examined the data in terms of the isotopic equilibrium attained under the conditions of Sutcliffe's experiments. Making allowance for the heterogeneity of the tissue by calculating the concentration of ions in the free space, Briggs was able to demonstrate that an efflux of potassium occurs simultaneously with a much higher rate of influx. The analysis showed that the fall in net flux, as the external potassium concentration falls and the vacuolar concentration rises, is mainly due to a rising efflux. In a similar manner it is possible to show that, in the presence of potassium cyanide, not only is the net flux into the cells very much reduced but so also are the rates of influx and efflux. The same is true of tissue placed in repeated changes of potassium bromide until the net uptake is reduced to a very low rate.

Such an analysis is extremely valuable, but in many ways it is an unsuitable method. The data presented by Sutcliffe concerned the simultaneous measurement of the chemical changes in potassium concentration and the changes in radioactivity of the external medium. The changes in the chemical and the radioactive potassium concentrations found by this method allowed Briggs to make his calculations of the rate of efflux and influx of potassium. The errors involved in the two sets of measurements appear to be large, for not all the data obtained by Sutcliffe are susceptible to such analysis. A more satisfactory method was used by Briggs, Hope and Pitman (1958b), who studied the potassium and sodium fluxes of beet discs which had been stored for seven days in distilled water. Before an experiment the discs were left for 2/4 hours in either potassium chloride or sodium chloride labelled with the appropriate isotope. When the ions in the free space were in equilibrium with those in the appropriate external solution, the influx and efflux of the two ions were studied, the former by chemical determination, the latter by radioactivity measurements. Allowance was made for the cation concentration in the free space. It was found that there is an efflux of both sodium and potassium during active accumulation from solutions containing each ion at a concentration of 5 m.equiv. per l. The efflux in the early stages is about $\frac{1}{25}$ of the influx. Later, the efflux of potassium tends to increase, while that of sodium continues to decrease. It appears that the influx and efflux of sodium are coupled. The same may be equally true of potassium fluxes in the early stages. However, the rise of potassium efflux during the later stages may be connected with the level of potassium in the vacuoles, for in an isolated experiment sodium efflux was observed to rise when the sodium content of the cells rose to a level comparable to that reached by potassium. These observations substantially confirm the earlier analysis made by Briggs (1957), though there appears to be a discrepancy in the fluxes when the internal concentration is high. Particularly interesting results were obtained from studies of the fluxes of potassium and sodium in media containing both ions (Fig. 7). The fluxes of sodium are barely affected by the presence of potassium (both at 5 m.equiv. per l.). The effect of sodium is to lower the influx and raise the efflux of potassium so reducing the net uptake to zero in the earlier stages. This effect disappears as the sodium concentration in the medium drops. Finally, Briggs *et al.* showed that the efflux and influx of potassium in bean roots are both large compared with the net flux. $_4$

These data for fluxes in beet discs are strikingly reminiscent of similar data for yeast cells. Exact comparison is not possible, but further research, on lines similar to previous work with yeast, suggests itself. More data are needed concerning fluxes of ions between higher plant tissues and the external medium. However, the sole fact of their demonstration is important and suggests new interpretations of data previously obtained with such tissues. Data concerning competition studies are the most susceptible to such new interpretation.

Epstein and Hagen (1952) studied the influence of various ions on rubidium uptake by barley roots. The analysis of their data depended upon the assumption that uptake of an ion is analagous to the combination between a substrate and an enzyme; in the case of ion uptake, the ion combines with a carrier which transports the ion into the interior of the cell, where the ion-carrier complex broke down in an irreversible manner. This assumption allowed the use of a kinetic analysis identical to that used by Lineweaver and Burk (1934) for enzyme action. Since this was so, the data were plotted in a similar manner; in this case, the reciprocal of the amount of ion taken up in a given time being plotted against the reciprocal of the concentration of ion in the external medium. Epstein and Hagen examined the results so plotted and drew conclusions as to whether ions competed for the same site of uptake or reduced uptake in an uncompetitive manner. This interpretation is exactly analogous to the Lineweaver and Burk analysis of competitive and uncompetitive inhibition of enzyme action. Epstein and Hagen concluded from their analysis that potassium, rubidium and calcium ions are bound to the same sites or reactive centres. With sodium, two types

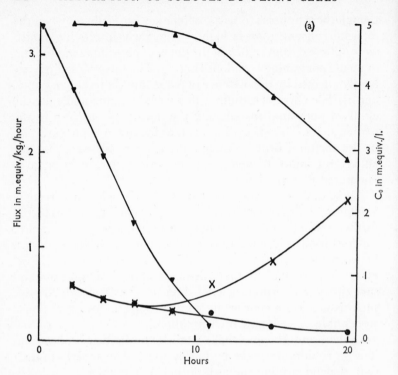

FIG. 7. Potassium fluxes in beet discs: (*a*) Immersed in a solution
containing potassium and sodium ions each initially 5 m. equiv.
per *l*. and subsequently as shown.

of site are involved. At low concentrations of sodium, the sites
which are involved do not bind rubidium. At higher concentrations of sodium, additional sites are brought into play which
also bind rubidium. Similarly, at higher concentrations of
rubidium, the uptake of this latter ion involves sites which also
bind sodium.

The correctness of this approach must be now questioned in
view of the possibility of several fluxes being involved in the
establishment of any observed net uptake. As has been seen with
beet tissue, sodium may reduce the net uptake of potassium by
increasing efflux as well as decreasing influx. Epstein and Hagen
made their analysis on the assumption that net uptake is
equivalent to influx. Since, however, this may not be so, such an

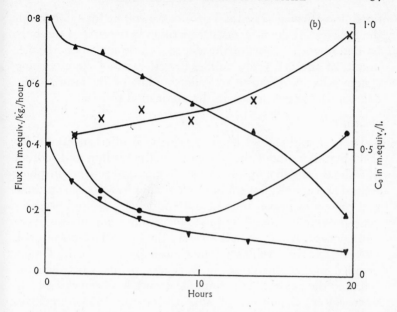

(b) As (a), but C_0 for potassium initially 1 m. equiv. per l.
(▲), potassium concentration; (▼), sodium concentration;
(×), influx; (●), efflux (Briggs, Hope and Pitman, 1958b).

analysis now appears to be untenable. A much more complex
experimental approach with measurements of both influx and
efflux of ions is required. Likewise the complete interpretation of
the data of Sutcliffe (1957) requires a knowledge of separate
fluxes. Sutcliffe has criticised the work of Epstein and Hagen and
has offered an algebraic explanation of the competitive effects of
ions. This explanation is based upon the observation made by
Sutcliffe that the total cation absorbed from mixtures is the
same as from a single salt solution of the same concentration.
The ion balance so achieved is unlikely to be due solely to
changed rates of influx. The results of Briggs *et al.* suggest that
the situation is more complicated than this. If their data apply
to this situation, as they should, the beet tissue should show a
much greater efflux of potassium from an equimolar solution of
potassium chloride and sodium chloride than from a single
solution of potassium chloride at the same concentration. Influx
should also be much lower. The fluxes of sodium should be very

much less affected. The total net uptake will be the same for all these fluxes. At the moment competition between ions can only be described in terms of the effects of one ion upon the net uptake of another. Only a fuller investigation of the absorbing system is likely to lead to an understanding of the nature of the competition between ions in the absorption process.

Animal cells

There is and should be no necessity to offer an excuse for including data about the movements of potassium and sodium in animal cells in any discussion of such movements in plant cells. The very elegant studies by animal physiologists on these movements in nerve, muscle and epithelial cells and erythrocytes provide for the plant physiologist many stimulating ideas and concepts which should increase the breadth of his outlook towards his own problems. The studies are noteworthy for the detailed measurements of the various ion fluxes between the cells and their external medium. The work has been extensively reviewed by a number of authors (Glynn, 1957 and 1959; Hodgkin, 1958; Ussing, 1960). Only the salient features will be referred to in this discussion.

The propogation of an impulse along a nerve* involves the temporary reversal of the membrane permeability from a resting state, in which the membrane is as much as one hundred times more permeable to potassium than sodium, to an active state, in which sodium enters over thirty times more easily than potassium, the permeability changes being controlled in a regenerative way by the membrane potential and timed so that first sodium enters and then potassium leaves the fibres. If the nerve cell is to continue to conduct impulses over long periods of time, it must possess a mechanism for pumping out sodium and for reabsorbing potassium, and indeed such movements are found to occur during the recovery period. Similar ion movements occur in erythrocytes. When erythrocytes are transferred to low temperatures, there is a fall in their potassium content and a rise in their sodium content. This process can be reversed if the cells are incubated at 37° with glucose.

---

* Unless otherwise stated, all the data for nerve cells has been obtained with the giant axons of the cuttle fish, *Sepia* and the squid, *Loligo*. Similarly, unless otherwise stated, the data for erythrocytes should be taken as data for human erythrocytes.

It is clear that the evidence which is available is very much in favour of these ion movements being brought about by active transport. Thus for red cells, glucose is necessary for these movements, and they are inhibited by sodium fluoride and iodoacetate (but not however by anoxia, cyanide or DNP, presumably because the movements derive their energy from glycolysis). While ion binding can explain the high cellular content of potassium, it cannot explain the low cellular content of sodium, unless it were postulated that a very large fraction of the cell water is bound. Furthermore, ion binding will not explain a number of results obtained from studying ion fluxes, especially the most exciting discovery that sodium efflux is greater when potassium is present in the external medium. It is difficult to envisage how potassium outside the cell could affect the binding of sodium inside. The same holds true for nerve cells (though for these cells it appears that aerobic metabolism provides the energy for the ion movements, since sodium efflux and potassium influx are inhibited by anoxia, cyanide and DNP), where intracellular binding of the ions has been shown to be incompatible with the observed movements of the ions through the axoplasm. If Ussing's equation (Chapter 2)

$$\frac{\phi_{\text{inwards}}}{\phi_{\text{outwards}}} = \frac{a_0}{a_i} e^{zF\Delta E/RT}$$

is applied to the sodium fluxes in nerve cells (assuming equal activity coefficients in the axoplasm and sea water which is used as the external medium), it appears that only from 0·5 to 2 per cent. of the outwards sodium flux can be reasonably ascribed to a purely passive diffusion process.

From such data as this, there is very good evidence that potassium ions are actively transported into, and sodium ions are actively transported out of both nerve cells and erythrocytes. On the basis of the observed effect of potassium on sodium efflux and the similarity of action of inhibitors on both sodium efflux and potassium influx, it is possible to conclude that the same mechanism brings about both fluxes. The attractive possibility has arisen that there is a tight coupling between sodium and potassium movements—one sodium ion being extruded for one potassium ion being taken in. This should not be taken to mean that the sodium efflux must equal the potassium influx or that the former should fall to zero in the absence of external potassium. In addition to the active efflux, there may be a passive component of sodium efflux which could continue when active efflux has ceased.

Glynn (1956) has investigated the linkage between the efflux of sodium and the influx of potassium in erythrocytes. The reduction in sodium efflux which is brought about by the removal of potassium from the external medium is much less than for nerve cells, complete absence of potassium reducing efflux by about one-third. It can be concluded, from the measurements of sodium efflux over a wide range of external potassium concentrations in the presence and in the absence of glucose, that sodium efflux in erythrocytes is made up of separate active and passive components and the active component is completely inhibited by the removal of potassium ions from the outside medium. The active components of both potassium influx and sodium efflux vary in a similar manner over a range of potassium concentrations. The half-maximal rate for both fluxes occurs with just over 2 mM, while the maximum rate is reached with around 10 mM potassium in the external medium. This evidence, together with the instantaneous nature of the changes in sodium efflux brought about by the changes in potassium concentration, indicates a direct linkage between the two transport processes and that probably a one to one exchange of ions occurs.

The linkage between potassium influx and sodium efflux does not appear to be at all rigid in nerve cells, since the latter is found to continue at about its normal rate when all ions are removed from the external medium and tonicity is maintained with glucose. Under these conditions, sodium is no longer moving against a concentration gradient; nevertheless this sodium efflux is blocked by DNP. There is no pH change in the external medium, so exchange of sodium ions for hydrogen ions can be eliminated. However, it is difficult to be sure that the potassium concentration immediately outside the membrane has not been raised by leakage of potassium to an extent which allows a coupled movement of sodium and potassium ions to continue.

Together with the active fluxes, there are passive movements of sodium and potassium ions in both directions across the membrane, the movement of sodium ions predominantly inward and that of potassium ions predominantly outward. It might be expected that the passive flux would be proportional to the driving force for that flux, i.e. to the electrochemical gradient. Analysis of such a flux can be made with the aid of Ussing's equation. It will be seen from an inspection of the equation that it is necessary to know the electrical potential difference (ΔE) across the cell membrane. For nerve cells, this presents no major practical difficulty and can be measured directly. On the other hand, it is impossible to measure directly this component for erythrocytes. Nevertheless, it is possible to derive a value for the electrical potential from measurements of the concentrations of chloride ions within the cell and in the external medium. Since the chloride ions are in diffusion equilibrium across the membrane, the following holds

$$\Delta E = \frac{RT}{zF} \ln \frac{Cl_0}{Cl_i}.$$

For erythrocytes of horse, the passive influx of potassium calculated from the observed passive efflux (net efflux minus active efflux) agrees very well with the observed value. Thus it is very probable that for these cells the fluxes are brought about by passive diffusion (Shaw, 1955). This is not so for human erythrocytes; nor can the fluxes be explained by the mechanism which brings about the passive fluxes of potassium ions in nerve cells. Hodgkin and Keynes (1955) found that the flux ratio for potassium, when the axons are poisoned with DNP, is very much greater than would be predicted from Ussing's equation. Furthermore, at constant membrane potential, an increase in the external potassium concentration reduces the potassium efflux. They showed that this type of behaviour is to be expected, if the potassium ions move through the membrane in single file along a narrow channel or series of special sites.

The passive sodium fluxes in human erythrocytes show a flux ratio less than that predicted by Ussing's equation. The evidence available suggests that the passive efflux of sodium may be reduced when the external sodium concentration is reduced to a low value. It is possible that *exchange diffusion* may be operating. This process, first postulated by Ussing (1947), may

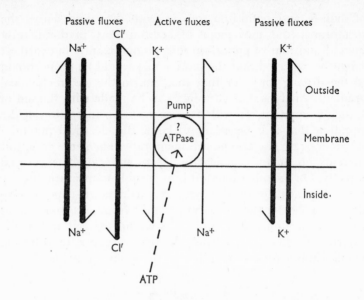

FIG. 8. A very much simplified schematic representation of the ionic interchanges across the membranes of nerve cells and erythrocites.

be described as follows. The cell membrane is not very permeable to the free diffusion of the ion in question. However, the membrane contains a carrier which can combine with the ion (in this case, sodium) to form a complex, and this complex, in contrast to the free carrier, is able to move across the membrane. It is not anticipated that this provides the only means whereby sodium efflux can occur, but it is clear that this offers a mechanism which can account for the increase in sodium efflux with increasing sodium concentration in the external medium. It is important to realise that there is no violation of thermodynamic principles in that such a mechanism brings about a rapid rate of flux *against* a concentration gradient. The movement of the ion concerned in one direction is balanced by the movement of the ion in the opposite direction—with the result that the net work done is nil. The actual molecular basis of exchange diffusion may well be other than described.

The results which have just been described (which are summarised in Fig. 8) are relevant to the observations on potassium and sodium movements between plant cells and their environment. Ussing (1960) has pointed out that, while the coupling of the active influx of potassium ions with the active extrusion of sodium ions has only been demonstrated for a few tissues, the presence of such a coupled transport system would explain the alkali ion distribution which has been measured in a variety of animal cells. It is possible that in some cases the hydrogen ion rather than the potassium ion may serve as a partner for sodium. Thus tubular acidification in the kidney seems to depend upon a forced exchange of sodium ions against hydrogen ions.

As yet, no evidence has been specifically sought for coupled movements of this type in plant cells, though there are indications that such a line of investigation might be profitable. For instance, it is likely that potassium influx is coupled to hydrogen extrusion in yeast cells. Sodium ions may also have a marked affinity for the mechanism extruding hydrogen ions and, if sodium efflux is brought about by such a mechanism, this may account for the lack of correlation between the observed effects of various inhibitors on sodium loss and upon potassium efflux from yeast cells. The potassium-sodium balance in yeast cells is not affected by the presence of up to 10^{-3} M strophanthin K in the external medium (D. H. Jennings and G. A. Souter, unpublished data) in contrast to animal cells where the movements of these ions is markedly sensitive to cardiac glycosides (see Chapter 5).

Though the indications are propitious for the finding of a coupled transport system in yeast cells, it appears from the experimental evidence that sodium ions are extruded from large algal cells independently of any movement of potassium ions. However, this data must be viewed with a certain caution, in view of a number of observations which have been made upon the transport of sodium ions across the epithelial layer of frog skin. Sodium ions are transported inward through the skin without any potassium being actively transported from the inside solutions to that bathing the outside of the skin. Nevertheless, potassium ions in the inside bathing solution are absolutely necessary for sodium transport. Recent work (Ussing, 1960) suggests that potassium is in fact the active exchange partner for sodium in frog skin but the potassium ions

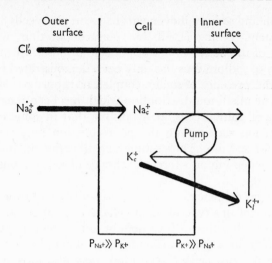

FIG. 9. A schematic representation of the ionic interchanges across the membranes of a frog epithelial cell.
Thick arrows represent passive fluxes; thin arrows,
active fluxes (Ussing, 1960).

move in a closed circuit, being 'pumped' into the epithelial cells
from the inside bathing solution and returning again to the
latter by passive transport (Fig. 9). Since all the studies on the
potassium and sodium fluxes in large algal cells have been made
with potassium ions in the external medium, it is to be expected
that such a situation would be overlooked.

There may be experimental difficulties attending the analysis
of potassium and sodium fluxes in plant cells other than the
large algal cells, since it may prove impossible to measure the
electrical potential across the cytoplasmic membrane not only
directly, because the cells are too small, but also indirectly,
since anions such as chloride ions do not seem to be in diffusion
equilibrium across the plasma membranes. Furthermore, as has
already been pointed out, the plant cannot be considered as a
homogeneous sytem with respect to alkali ions. While Gold and
Solomon (1955) have presented evidence that a small fraction
of cellular sodium of human erythrocytes exchanges at a very
much slower rate than the majority of sodium ions within the
cell, in general, animal cells can be considered homogeneous

with respect to potassium and sodium ions. Sufficient evidence
has already been presented to show that plant cells cannot be so
considered and that there are at least three compartments (free
space, protoplasmic non-free space and the vacuole) each with
their characteristic but differing flux rates. As has already been
emphasised in Chapter 3, the determination of the fluxes across
the plasma membranes cannot therefore be a matter of direct
measurement.

H

CHAPTER 7

BIVALENT CATION UPTAKE

In the section on potassium and sodium uptake by plant cells, attention was drawn to the data of Conway and Duggan (1958) which suggested that the uptake of magnesium by yeast cells is by the same mechanism as that responsible for the accumulation of the alkali cations, potassium, rubidium, caesium, sodium and lithium, given in the order of their rate of uptake. The uptake of calcium was also suggested to be by the same mechanism (Conway and Duggan, 1956). Conway and Beary (1958) made a detailed study of the uptake of magnesium by this mechanism. They showed that the uptake of magnesium increases with concentration up to about 500 mM, which contrasts with the concentration of potassium ions (2 mM) needed for maximum uptake of potassium, demonstrating the greater affinity of potassium for the uptake mechanism. Magnesium ions are exchanged for hydrogen ions during the uptake process. Magnesium once inside the yeast cell cannot be displaced by high concentrations of potassium ions in the external medium. Magnesium uptake is inhibited by anoxia, azide and cyanide. Magnesium uptake is also inhibited by DNP, provided that magnesium is present as magnesium chloride. However, when magnesium acetate, propionate, butyrate or valerate are used there is no inhibition. The effects of anoxia, azide and cyanide are independent of the accompanying anions.

The rate of potassium uptake under anaerobic conditions differs little from that under aerobic conditions. Since this is so, the inhibition of magnesium by anoxia suggest that, either magnesium is not absorbed by the mechanism responsible for the absorption of potassium ions, or the uptake of magnesium is more complicated than appeared from the original observation of Conway and Duggan. The associated anions are obviously significant in this problem. The differential effect of DNP, depending on the presence of chloride or acetate, has been referred to, but the inhibition of magnesium uptake by potassium also seems to depend in part upon the anion present. A curious feature of the inhibition curve of magnesium uptake by potassium is that it descends more slowly from the 50 per cent. inhibition level than would be expected on the basis of Michaelis-Menton kinetics. Whatever the rationale for using kinetic analysis, this divergence is not observed when chloride ions are present instead of acetate ions. A key to this question concerning the uptake of magnesium would lie in a study of the effect of magnesium on potassium uptake. One would expect, if these two ions were absorbed by the same mechanism, that magnesium would inhibit the uptake of potassium in the same way as potassium ions inhibit the uptake of magnesium, though the concentrations involved would differ in the two cases, depending on the specificity of the mechanism for the two ions.

Whatever the nature of the 'carrier' proposed by Conway and Duggan, an important characteristic appears to be its property of being a general carrier for cations. Data will be presented in the next chapter which suggest tentatively that such a mechanism may exist in barley roots. However, one must be cautious in generalising about this. Epstein and Leggett (1954) studied the absorption of calcium, strontium and barium ions by barley roots. It appeared from their investigations that calcium, barium and strontium are absorbed by the same mechanism, but magnesium, if the ion is absorbed by barley roots, enters the cells by a different mechanism. The results of Kahn and Hanson (1957) indicate that the affinity of calcium and potassium for the uptake mechanism may differ from tissue to tissue.

While yeast can absorb magnesium ions in exchange for hydrogen ions by a mechanism which, although strongly specific for potassium ions, can bring about the uptake of a number of cations, there is also another mechanism responsible for magnesium and manganese uptake, which is strongly specific for these two ions and which is related to the phosphate metabolism of the cell. Rothstein, Hayes, Jennings and Hooper (1958) showed that manganous ions are rapidly absorbed by yeast cells in the presence of phosphate, glucose and potassium. Originally, Rothstein (1954) suggested that the magnesium and manganous ions are transported into the yeast cell as a soluble phosphate-complex. However, Rothstein *et al.* showed that the absorption of phosphate and potassium by the yeast cell is the important factor in their effect on manganese uptake and not their presence in the external medium. There appears to be no fixed stoichiometric relationship between manganese uptake and phosphate and potassium uptake. Phosphate is always absorbed more rapidly than manganese, and the rate of uptake of phosphate is unaffected by manganous ion. The absorption of manganese, however, can continue when all the phosphate is absorbed and, after a period of time, may exceed the phosphate absorption. The absorption of manganous ions occurs in the absence of potassium ions (phosphate must be present) but is markedly stimulated in their presence. But, whereas phosphate has a stimulatory effect over the whole range of concentrations, above a concentration of 20 mM, potassium ions are markedly inhibitory. While the stimulation of manganese uptake at the lower potassium concentrations is a direct effect of the stimulation of phosphate uptake, the inhibition of manganese uptake at the higher concentrations is ascribable to a large cation excess within the cells, as a result of the high rate of potassium uptake in the presence of glucose. Jennings, Hooper and Rothstein (1958) further categorised the influence of phosphate and potassium on manganese uptake by yeast cells. They showed that absorption of manganese can be isolated in time from the absorption of phosphate. Cells pretreated with glucose, potassium ions and phosphate, then washed thoroughly and resuspended in a potassium and phosphate-free buffer are capable of absorbing manganese without delay. In fact, this treatment does not result in any reduction in the amount of manganese absorbed compared with the quantity absorbed during a similar period of time when phosphate is present. However, as cells are allowed to stand, there is a loss of absorptive power. This loss of absorptive power is dependent upon the metabolism of the cells and is particularly dependent on the rate of glycolysis, for cells lose their absorptive power most rapidly in presence of fermentable sugars.

By using the pretreatment mechanism just described, Jennings *et al.* were able to study the properties of the manganese transport system in isolation from the process of phosphate uptake which is necessary for its initiation. Inhibitor studies with sodium acetate, redox dyes and arsenate revealed

BIVALENT CATION UPTAKE 109

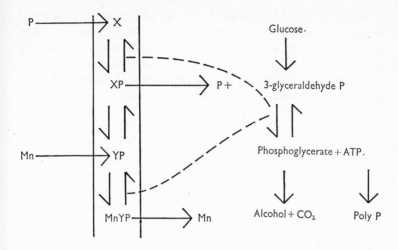

FIG. 10. A scheme for the absorption of manganous ions and phosphate ions into the yeast cell (Jennings, Hooper & Rothstein, 1957).

parallel effects on manganese absorption and on phosphate absorption. Jennings *et al.* postulated that both phosphate and manganese are transferred into the yeast cell in an essentially irreversible manner by two systems, which are coupled in an unknown way to glycolysis at the 3-phosphoglyceraldehyde dehydrogenase step. Yeast cells ordinarily absorb phosphate only after a lag period of about thirty minutes, but, if pretreated with glucose and potassium, no delay occurs. It was suggested, therefore, that a phosphate carrier is synthesised during glycolysis. The manganese carrier is also a phosphorylated compound formed in the cell membrane as a direct product of the phosphate-transferring system and chemically related to the phosphate carrier (Fig. 10). This would account for the similar sensitivity of both phosphate and manganese uptake to the same inhibitors. As the ability of the yeast cell to absorb manganese is transient, the synthesis of the manganese carrier must be a reversible reaction. The exact chemical nature of the carrier is unknown. Its absence in cells undergoing glycolysis in the absence of phosphate eliminates glycolytic intermediates as possible candidates, and, since most of the phosphate which is absorbed can be accounted for as poly-phosphates and glycolytic intermediates (Juni, Kamen, Reiner and Spiegelman, 1948; Wiame, 1949), the amount of carrier must be small. The properties of the carrier seem to be very similar to many phosphorylating enzymes. There is no evidence that this mechanism acts in other plant tissues.

CHAPTER 8

THE EFFECT OF BIVALENT CATIONS UPON THE UPTAKE OF ALKALI CATIONS

For a number of decades, it has been recognised that bivalent cations (most particularly, calcium ions) can have a marked effect upon the permeability properties of living cells, both animal and plant. In spite of the venerable nature of the problem, little progress has been made towards its elucidation. It might even be said that this very venerability has given to the problem a certain mystique.

It would be generally agreed that the lineage of this problem owes its origin to the now classical studies of Jaques Loeb on the development of the eggs of the marine fish *Fundulus* (Loeb, 1906, for a summary of these studies). Development of these eggs is inhibited, if they are put immediately after fertilisation into a pure solution of sodium chloride having the same concentration as that of this salt in sea water. However, if a small quantity of the salt of a bivalent cation such as calcium, strontium, magnesium or even lead is added to the sodium chloride solution, development of the egg into the embryo is able to proceed (Table 6). The result depends only upon the cations

TABLE 6

The effect of calcium in removing the inhibition of the development of *Fundulus* eggs in the presence of sodium chloride (100 ml. $\frac{5}{8}$M solution)

(Loeb, 1906)

Quantity of $\frac{M}{64}$ CaSO$_4$ added (ml.)	Percentage of the *Fundulus* eggs which form an embryo
—	0
0·5	3
1·0	3
2·0	20
4·0	75
8·0	70

present, as different salts of the same metal are able to act equally well as 'depoisoners'. Osterhout (1906) showed that certain marine plants which can live for some time in distilled water die considerably sooner in a solution of sodium chloride isotonic with sea water. The presence of a small quantity of calcium chloride along with the sodium chloride enables the plants to live nearly as long as in distilled water (1 ml. $\frac{3}{8}$ M calcium chloride to 100 ml. $\frac{3}{8}$ M sodium chloride). The addition of a little potassium chloride as well enables the plants to live longer than in distilled water, while with the further addition of some magnesium chloride the plants live as long as they would in sea water. The reduction in the toxicity of one ion by another in this manner is termed *antagonism*.

It is unfortunate that the meaning of this term has become blurred in the years subsequent to its first use in this sense. The term has been used to describe a variety of observations which are similar as regards the total situation but which may be ascribed to a number of causes. It is clear that the original meaning of the term implied the lowering of the 'toxic' effect of a solute on the viability of the cell by the presence in low concentration of another solute in the medium external to the cell involved. Reduction of the toxic effect of a solute by another could indeed be through permeability phenomena, and, in fact, Loeb showed that this must be the case in his experiments with *Fundulus* eggs. Unfortunately, the postulation of the site of action of the antagonising solute has led to the use of antagonism for permeation phenomena *sensu strictu*. When this has happened, it is not always clear whether the reduction in the uptake of one solute by another is accompanied by greater longevity of the cells involved. This criticism might be considered pedantic, but it should be realised that a very real distinction exists. Unless there is some knowledge about the metabolism of the cells involved, the reduction in the uptake of a solute by another could be through the inhibitory action of this latter solute on metabolism rather than by a direct effect on the permeability properties of the cell with respect to the uptake of the former solute. Furthermore, the original concept of antagonism envisaged that the antagonising compound need only be present in low concentrations relative to the concentration of the toxic solute. Where the term has been applied

solely to permeability phenomena, it is not unusual to find
that the concentrations of the participating solutes are little
different.

It should be clear that the term is used to define a
specific and rather limited situation. Many of the early studies
on the effect of bivalent cations upon the uptake of alkali cations
were concerned with the antagonistic aspects of the relationships, often for the reason that many of the methods for
measuring rate of solute uptake used such factors as viability of
cells, loss of pigment or colour changes in the vacuole as indices
of the amount of solute absorbed. While many such studies have
an intrinsic interest, it is more pertinent to the present discussion
to consider experimental evidence from later work, where the
solute uptake is measured by determining changes in solute
concentration. Such work tells little about antagonism but is
more consistent with physiological reasoning in that it is dealing,
as far as possible, with one parameter of the system, namely
permeability. In doing so, it has been possible to show that the
relationship between bivalent ions and alkali cations with
respect to this parameter shows a considerable complexity.

Viets (1944) showed that the absorption of potassium and
bromide ions by excised barley roots from a 5 mM solution of
potassium bromide can be increased by the presence of calcium
in the external medium up to 200 m.equiv. per l. of calcium
chloride. Above this concentration of calcium, there is a
decrease in the uptake of both potassium and bromide ions—
potassium uptake being the more inhibited, dropping to a level
below the value obtained when no calcium is present. Calcium
uptake increases with increasing concentration of the ions in the
external solution (Fig. 11). Viets showed that other polyvalent
cations, magnesium, cobalt, strontium, barium and aluminium
can also stimulate the uptake of potassium and bromide ions.

Overstreet, Jacobson and Handley (1952) confirmed these
results and further showed that potassium ions inhibit the
uptake of calcium ions from an 0·0005 N calcium chloride
solution. There is no evidence of a stimulation of calcium
uptake over the range of potassium concentrations which were
tested (up to 100 m.equiv. per l. potassium chloride). Fawzy,
Overstreet and Jacobson (1954) showed that a number of
multivalent ions, e.g. aluminium, cerium and lanthanum, are

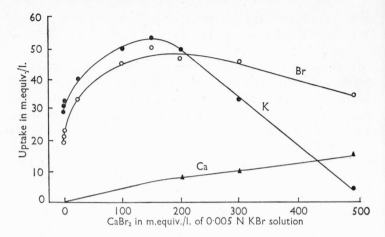

FIG. 11. The absorption of potassium, bromide and calcium ions by excised barley roots placed in aerated solutions as indicated for 8¼ hours (Viets, 1944).

also capable of stimulating the uptake of potassium ions by excised barley roots.

Middleton and Russell (1958) found that strontium ions at 25 m.equiv. per l. can increase, by as much as 80 per cent., the absorption of rubidium ions by carrot discs (stored for 7 days in aerated distilled water previous to an experiment) from a solution of rubidium chloride (3·2 m.equiv. per l.) over a 24-hour period.

It is clear from these experiments that this is a non-specific phenomenon—bivalent and trivalent cations stimulating the uptake of alkali cations. Middleton and Russell suggested that the bivalent cations, by virtue of the fact that they are more readily associated with the fixed anions of the free space, prevent the univalent ions from being so associated, in this manner increasing the concentration of these latter ions at the sites of absorption at the outer region of the cytoplasm. The displacement of the univalent ions from their association with fixed anions of the free space results in the acceleration of the rate of movement towards the sites of entry into the non-free space. Critical examination of this suggestion is difficult, but such an examination should involve experiments with discs of different thickness. Since the above suggestion implicates the rate of diffusion of the alkali cations within the tissue as an important factor in controlling the uptake of the ions, variations in disc-size should provide a means of altering the length of the diffusion path which is available to these ions.

Jacobson and his co-workers (Fawzy *et al.*, 1954; Jacobson, Moore and Hannapel, 1960) have provided another explanation, for which there is much more evidence, however not necessarily exclusive of that given by Middleton and Russell. In essence, the explanation is as follows. The multivalent cations, by becoming preferentially associated with the free space, reduce the concentration of hydrogen ions in that region. The pH that results is more favourable to the process of absorption of the alkali cations into the non-free space. The evidence for this explanation is two-fold. Potassium uptake is markedly reduced as the hydrogen ion concentration in the external medium is increased. At a pH of 3 and under, potassium ions are lost from the roots. Jacobson *et al.* (1960) also measured the change of pH brought about by the presence of roots in solutions of various monovalent and bivalent ions at the same original concentration and pH. The roots were given no other treatment except the usual preparatory washing before placing in the appropriate solution. In order to avoid complications induced by metabolic absorption, only pH values at the end of two minutes were considered. The presence of bivalent cations results in lower final pH values, indicating that these ions are more effective than monovalent cations in excluding hydrogen ions from the free space (Table, 7).

There is little evidence on which to base a hypothesis which will explain the inhibition of potassium uptake at the higher concentrations of calcium. Viets (1954) ascribed his results to an unfavourable osmotic effect, but, although the roots lose weight under these conditions, calcium uptake appears to be unaffected and continues to rise with increasing concentration of calcium. Overstreet *et al.* (1952) showed that the effect is unlikely to be osmotic. They studied the potassium uptake by barley roots from solutions of different potassium concentration in the presence of 0·01 N calcium chloride. At the lowest concentration of potassium chloride (10^{-5} N), calcium completely inhibits the uptake of potassium. With increasing concentrations of potassium chloride there is an increased uptake of potassium, such that the inhibitory action of calcium is abolished and the uptake of potassium is stimulated in the manner referred to above. Since potassium uptake can be increased in this manner, injurious effects ascribable to osmotic phenomena cannot be the explanation of the inhibition of potassium uptake by calcium ions.

TABLE 7

The effect of excised barley roots upon pH of various salt solutions initially adjusted to pH 4·00

(Jacobson, Moore and Hannapel, 1960)

Added Salt*	pH†
None	4·79
LiBr	4·71
NaBr	4·72
NH_4Br	4·71
KBr	4·69
RbBr	4·70
CsBr	4·74
$BeBr_2$	4·30
$MgBr_2$	4·65
$CaBr_2$	4·59
$SrBr_2$	4·64
$BaBr_2$	4·60
$AlBr_3$	4·00
$LaBr_3$	4·31
$ThBr_4$	4·28

* 1 m. equiv. per l. of indicated salt added to a solution of 1 m. equiv. per l. KBr.

† pH measured 2 minutes after the addition of 20 g. excised roots to 100 ml. of solution.

The most reasonable explanation for the present is that potassium and calcium ions can be absorbed by a common mechanism similar in properties to that proposed by Conway and Duggan (1956 and 1958) for yeast cells. The uptake mechanism would be strongly specific for potassium and very much less so for calcium. This appears to be so, for calcium uptake from 0·005 N calcium chloride is markedly reduced by concentrations of potassium which are very much lower than those calcium concentrations required to reduce, by the same amount, potassium uptake from an equivalent concentration of potassium chloride.

Unless experimental evidence is provided to the contrary, the effect of bivalent cations on anion uptake can only be ascribed to the effect of bivalent cations on the alkali cation balance (and hence the total ion balance) within the cells.

Even though it can be shown that the stimulation of potassium uptake by calcium ions is a non-specific phenomenon, certain evidence singled out calcium ions, from among other bivalent cations, as being a little more effective and also possessing special properties with respect to the permeability of cells to potassium. Viets (1944) noted that calcium ions appeared to stimulate potassium uptake to a greater extent than other bivalent cations at an equivalent concentration in the external medium. Fawzy et al. (1954) noted that calcium ions appeared to be more effective than all other cations tested in arresting the loss of potassium from barley roots, when they are subjected to solutions of markedly acid pH. Such observations as these were instrumental in encouraging Jacobson and his co-workers to make an intensive study of the effect of calcium on the uptake of alkali cations. Whether such observations are part of the phenomena about to be described remains to be seen.

The major finding which has arisen from the experiments in Jacobson's laboratory concerns the effect of calcium on the mutual interference by alkali cations on their individual rates of uptake. It was found that calcium ions can reverse the inhibitory effect of lithium and sodium on potassium uptake (Jacobson, Moore and Hannapel, 1960; Jacobson, Hannapel, Moore and Schaedle, 1961). Fig. 12 shows the relationship between calcium, potassium and sodium ions. It will be noted that calcium is only effective below a certain sodium concentration, in this case under 5 m.equiv. per l. sodium bromide. The relationship between calcium and the potassium-lithium interaction appears to be different from the relationship with the potassium-sodium interaction. Although calcium ions inhibit the uptake of both lithium and sodium ions in the presence of potassium, in the absence of potassium ions only the uptake of lithium is inhibited (Fig. 13).

The contrasting behaviour of these two ions may be partly

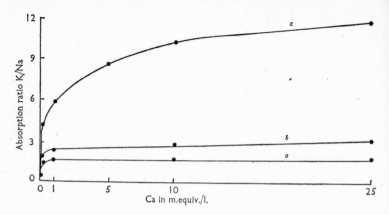

FIG. 12. The effect of calcium ions upon the ratio of absorption of potassium to sodium by excised barley roots. All solutions contained 5 m. equiv. potassium bromide per *l*. In addition, there was 1, 5 and 15 m. equiv. sodium bromide per *l*. respectively in treatments *a*, *b* and *c*. The absorption period was 3 hours; 1 g. of roots to a litre of solution; the pH maintained at 6·0, the temperature 25° (Jacobson, Hannapel, Moore and Schaedle, 1961).

explained by the chemical properties of lithium ions. It has already been pointed out in Chapter 6, with respect to alkali ion balance in *Porphyra* cells, that lithium ions resemble the ions of the alkaline earth cations in many of their properties. If this is so, the inhibition of lithium uptake by calcium ions may be allied to the phenomenon of reduction of magnesium uptake by barley roots in the presence of calcium ions (Moore, Overstreet and Jacobson, 1961). The rate of uptake of both lithium and magnesium are approximately equal, being half that of potassium, sodium and rubidium. The uptake of both lithium and magnesium ions, when in solution at 5 m.equiv. per l., are inhibited to the same extent by calcium ions at a concentration of 0·50 m.equiv. per l.

Epstein (1961) has confirmed these observations and has provided some interesting additional data. He found that the inhibitory action of sodium on the uptake of rubidium by barley roots is also overcome by the presence of calcium ions. A comparison of the effectiveness of other bivalent cations with respect to the suppression of the inhibitory action of sodium produced some surprising results, in that manganous ions were

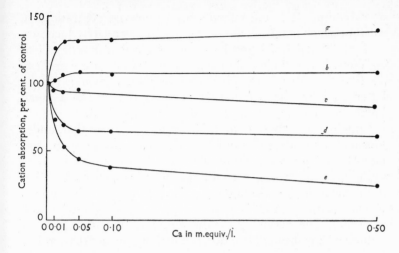

FIG. 13. The effect of small amounts of calcium on the absorption
of potassium sodium and lithium ions by excised barley roots.

    (a) Potassium from potassium bromide and sodium bromide.

    (b) Potassium from potassium bromide.

    (c) Sodium from sodium bromide.

    (d) Sodium from sodium bromide and potassium bromide.

    (e) Lithium from lithium bromide.

    All alkali metal salts were present at 5 m. equiv. per l., other-
wise the conditions were the same as those given for Fig. 12
(Jacobson, Hannapel, Moore and Schaedle, 1961).

nearly as effective as calcium ions, whereas magnesium
ions were singularly ineffective. Finally, it is significant
that calcium ions not only suppress the inhibitory action of
sodium ions on potassium uptake but also reduce the uptake of
sodium ions when potassium ions are also present.

Epstein emphasised that this situation differs from the
phenomenon first described by Viets (1944) in the following
respects. The effect of calcium ions is limited strictly to the
suppression of the inhibitory action of sodium ions upon the
uptake of either potassium or rubidium ions. The phenomenon
described by Viets concerned the actual stimulation of the
uptake of a specific alkali action. In the absence of sodium,
calcium ions at the low concentrations at which they are
present in solution have little effect on the uptake of potassium

or rubidium. It is the effectiveness of low concentrations of calcium which marks off the phenomenon observed by Jacobson *et al.* (1960 and 1961) and by Epstein from that first described by Viets. For in the former case, concentrations of the order of 3×10^{-4} N to 10^{-3} N are sufficient to be effective, whereas in the latter case for the stimulation of potassium uptake a much higher concentration—around 10^{-2} N—is required.

Epstein, on the basis of his findings, has suggested that, under 'normal' physiological conditions when calcium is present, uptake of potassium and rubidium is via two sites, one inhibited by sodium, the other largely indifferent to the presence of this ion in the medium. Uptake of sodium also involves two sites, one of which is largely indifferent to the presence of potassium and rubidium. The reasoning for the postulate that the uptake of sodium occurs through two sites is based on the fact that, at low potassium concentrations, there is a pronounced inhibition of sodium uptake, but, at higher concentrations of potassium, the response of sodium uptake to added increments of potassium becomes very slight. Similar reasoning applies for the postulate that there are two sites for potassium-rubidium uptake. Potassium uptake is markedly inhibited by low concentrations of sodium, but increasing concentrations bring no further inhibition. The evidence which suggests that potassium and rubidium uptake is through the same site has already been presented in Chapter 6.

The system can be characterised further, especially with respect to the presence of calcium ions. Thus:

Potassium-rubidium system (Fig. 14).

Site A: low affinity for potassium ions; the uptake of potassium is inhibited by sodium ions but the effect is mitigated (not however reversed) by calcium.

Site B: relatively high affinity for potassium ions; the uptake of potassium is inhibited by sodium ions, except when calcium ions are present, in which case uptake is unaffected.

Sodium system (Fig. 15):

Site C: low affinity for sodium ions; sodium uptake is largely inhibited by potassium ions when calcium ions are present.

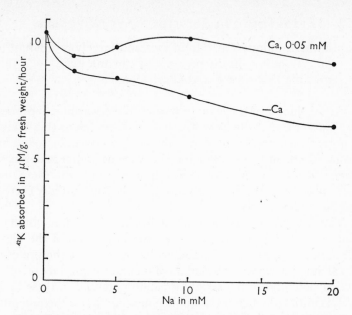

Fig. 14. The effectiveness of calcium in reversing the inhibition by sodium of the absorption of potassium by excised barley roots. Potassium concentration 1 mM; duration of experiment 1 hour; 1 g. barley roots to 100 ml. solution; 30° (Epstein, 1961).

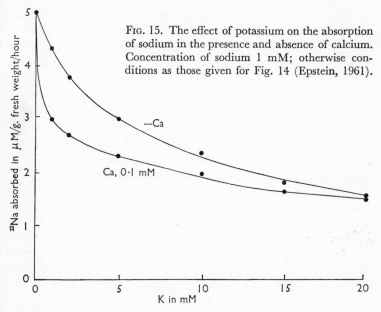

Fig. 15. The effect of potassium on the absorption of sodium in the presence and absence of calcium. Concentration of sodium 1 mM; otherwise conditions as those given for Fig. 14 (Epstein, 1961).

I

Site D: high affinity for sodium ions and largely indifferent to
potassium ions in the presence of calcium ions.
It is possible that sites A and C are identical.

At this juncture it is wise to re-iterate the warning expressed
in Chapter 6 that the interpretation of data such as this, which
involves measurements of net fluxes, must remain *sub judice*
unless there are also data for the various individual fluxes.
Nevertheless, in spite of this important proviso, there are
indications that this interpretation may be substantially correct
in a number of essentials.

The reasons for this line of thought come from data obtained
from an entirely different source—the large cells of the algae
Nitella and *Chara australis*. The evidence concerns the presence
of calcium ions in the external medium and the production of an
action potential in the cells. An action potential in these large
cells is initiated when the vacuole potential, that is the potential
difference between the vacuole sap and the external solution
across the cytoplasm, is depressed below a critical level. This
depression can be caused either by a passage of an electric
current from the vacuole to the bathing solution or by an
increase in the ionic concentration of the external solution
(Osterhout, 1931). When the potential difference is depressed
in this manner, the cell acts in an excitatory manner so that the
cytoplasm becomes depolarised. The action potential difference
is the potential difference which is measured under these
conditions. Action potentials can also be generated by a sudden
decrease in temperature or by mechanical shock (Osterhout,
1931; Osterhout and Hill, 1935). The most suitable method of
stimulation is by means of an electric current, which can be
controlled more easily than other types of stimuli. The electric
potential changes are measured in the manner usual to all such
studies on the P.D. across the cytoplasm of such cells.

A good example of the time course exhibited by an action
potential is given in Fig. 16. Findlay (1959) showed that the
action potential in the cytoplasm is almost identical with that
in the vacuole. Thus it appears that the action potential occurs
almost entirely across the outer cytoplasmic boundary.

Gaffey and Mullins (1958) using *Nitella* cells measured the
ion fluxes associated with the action potential. They found that

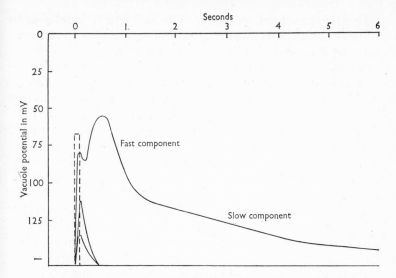

Fig. 16. The action potential measured in the vacuole of a *Nitella* cell. The response of the vacuole potential to two sub-threshold pulses and a suprathreshold pulse is shown. The broken line shows the potential applied between the vacuole and the bathing solution by the stimulating current. The two components in the action potential are indicated (Findlay, 1959).

the effect of stimulation is to increase by a factor of 20 to 30 times the resting fluxes of potassium and chloride ions. The sodium influx and efflux as well as the chloride influx are entirely unaffected by stimulation. The potassium influx is reduced to an immeasurable value, but this was believed to be due to an artifact of experimental procedure, since influx measurements, due to the complicating factor of exchange in the free space, are necessarily inaccurate in the presence of a large potassium efflux.

Gaffey and Mullins reported that the peak of the action potential is influenced by the concentration of chloride ions in the external medium. On the other hand, Hope (1961) reports that, of all the ions tested, only calcium ions are able to produce consistent changes in the peak level of the action potential of *Chara australis*. The ions tested were the cations sodium, potassium, magnesium, strontium and barium and the anions chloride, bromide, glucuronate and benzene sulphonate.

Hope has pointed out that, in order to test the effect of variations in concentration of a given ion, it is very important that the P.D. between the cell wall and the medium is kept constant. Hope and Walker (1961) found that, following a change in the total ion concentration in the external medium, the wall potential rapidly changes and that of the protoplast surface comes to equilibrium more slowly. These changes in wall potential can be eliminated by varying the concentration of an ion in conjunction with that of another ion of similar ionic charge, keeping the total ion concentration constant. Thus, the effect of different concentrations of calcium ions was tested by varying the concentration from 0·3 to 5 mN and at the same time varying the magnesium ion concentration in the reverse direction from 4·7 to 0 mN, the total concentration of the two ions being 5 mN. Hope showed that it is possible to explain the results of Gaffey and Mullins in terms of a changing wall P.D., though it must be admitted that certain assumptions have to be made with regard to their experimental procedure.

It should be apparent that a varied experimental attack is required for continuing this investigation. More information about flux data is required, especially for the movement of calcium ions during the action potential. While the study is intrinsically of great interest, the above data are also important because they provide a basis, albeit very tentative, for an experimental approach to the calcium, potassium and sodium interactions observed for barley roots. Mullins (1959) has suggested that the membrane of nerve cells contains long narrow pores which are filled in the resting state with potassium ions. Mullins has envisaged that the pore size changes during excitation, so that the majority of pores are filled with sodium ions. Thus the membrane acts as a potassium-electrode in the resting state and as a sodium-electrode in the excited state. Hope has suggested that this idea could be applied to *Chara australis* with calcium ions taking the place of sodium ions. However, he points out that any proposed mechanism, as well as providing for a reasonable explanation for the P.D.s which are observed, must account for the large increases in overall conduction which occur during the action potential (Cole and Curtis, 1938). Hope suggests that the situation appears to be such that more pores (all calcium-filled) are opened and then closed, rather than existing pores show a change in function. It is tempting to equate the calcium pores with those sites in barley roots with which calcium interacts and to equate those with which calcium is not associated with the sites in barley roots in which calcium ions are ineffective.

It is not possible to say how far the data presented above provide the basis for a complete explanation of the phenomenon of calcium-sodium antagonism. There is evidence that potassium ions must also be considered as playing an integral part in such a relationship. Eppley and Cyrus (1960) have shown that in diluted sea water the presence of calcium ions is very important for maintaining the potassium-sodium balance of the cells of *Porphyra perforata* and also for maintaining the fresh weight of the tissues. E. B. G. Jones (personal communication) has found that calcium ions can play an important role in bringing about the growth of the fungus *Cercospora salina* in media containing high concentrations of sodium ions. Such studies have also shown that, while permeability phenomena are also involved, the situation with regard to antagonism is probably not simple and that the direct effect of the ions on growth must also be considered. This must involve considerations of the actions of ions within the cell and naturally cannot be discussed further here.

Not all cells show the phenomenon whereby calcium ions can mitigate the interfering action of sodium on potassium uptake. Yeast cells do not show the phenomenon (D. H. Jennings and G. A. Souter, unpublished data). Furthermore, calcium ions may interact with the permeability mechanisms of plant cells in a variety of ways, as yet undetected.

CHAPTER 9

PHOSPHATE UPTAKE

Phosphate participates in many biochemical reactions. It is found combined with low molecular weight carbon compounds which are involved in intermediary metabolism and it is a component of many large molecules which are a part of the structural basis of cells. Consequently, investigators have not been surprised at the close relationship between metabolism and phosphate uptake. Nevertheless, one cannot conclude that the metabolic reactions involved in the incorporation of phosphate ions into organic compounds within a cell are those responsible for the uptake of phosphate by the same cell. In any study of phosphate uptake, unless otherwise proved, there has to be a clear distinction between the process involved in the increase in the overall phosphorus content of a cell and the incorporation of phosphorus into organic compounds within the same cell. This distinction has not always been clear, and, in consequence, there has been a tendency to equate the absorption of phosphate ions with those processes which are involved in metabolism of phosphate within cells.

The uptake of phosphate has been shown to be closely connected with metabolism in many cells. In yeast, the presence of sugar is necessary for the uptake of phosphate (Hevesy *et al.*, 1937). The same is true for phosphate uptake by *Streptococcus faecalis* (O'Kane and Umbreit, 1942) and *Staphylococcus aureus* (Hotchkiss, 1944).

In yeast, the uptake of phosphate is only appreciable in the presence of the fermentable sugars, glucose, fructose and mannose (Goodman and Rothstein, 1957). The uptake with glucose is just as rapid in aerobic as anaerobic conditions (Mullins, 1942). Respiration of alcohol supports an uptake of only 20 per cent. of that in the presence of glucose, while lactate, pyruvate and acetate can support only a low rate of uptake (Table 8). Other evidence that phosphate uptake is closely linked to fermentation rather than respiration is found in the temporal relationship of the processes. If glucose is added 30 minutes prior to phosphate, a steady rate of phosphate uptake is immediately established. If, however, the glucose and phosphate are added simultaneously, there is a 10 to 15 minute lag period before a steady rate of phosphate uptake is achieved. A similar lag period can be demonstrated for the attainment of the maximum rate of fermentation; no lag period is observed for respiration.

TABLE 8

The dependence of phosphate uptake by yeast upon a specific substrate. The experiments were carried out anaerobically. Yeast concentration, 100 mg. per ml.; substrate, 0·3 M; KCl, 0·02 M; H_3PO_4, 0·01−0·02 M; pH 4·5−5·0

(Goodman and Rothstein, 1957)

Substrate	Phosphate uptake in mM phosphate/kg. yeast
Glucose	254·8
Fructose	201·6
Mannose	161·4
Lactate	10·3
Pyruvate	9·1
Acetate	0
Ethyl Alcohol . . .	49·5

The connection between phosphate uptake and metabolism might be envisaged in several ways. Roberts and Roberts (1950) suggested, from their observations on phosphate uptake by *Escherichia coli*, that the absorption of the ion by the cell is through the synthesis of new compounds within the cell which are able to bind phosphate. Their hypothesis was based on the increased uptake of phosphate in the presence of glucose and potassium, the inhibition of uptake in the presence of phosphorylated sugars and the lack of exchange of phosphate once absorbed. Metabolism might play a more specific role, and this postulate could apply to yeast where the linkage of phosphate uptake and fermentation could be through the absorption of phosphate by esterification of 3-phosphoglyceraldehyde. On the other hand, a carrier could be produced during fermentation which would be responsible for the transport of phosphate ions into the cell, this carrier compound playing no part in the general metabolism of the cell. Finally, if phosphate ions are actively transported into the cell, metabolism will provide the energy for the absorption of phosphate, the energetic link being the only direct connection between the two processes.

Mitchell (1953 and 1954) has effectively disposed of the first postulate through a study of exchange phenomena in *Staphylococcus aureus*. Using ^{32}P, he observed a rate of exchange of 1·4 moles per g. cell dry weight per min. in resting cells. The net flux is less than 1 per cent. of the exchange flux. When the cells are allowed to respire in the presence of glucose, there is a net flux of phosphate directed inwards at a rate of 1·4 moles per g. per min., and the outward flux falls virtually to zero. If the uptake of phosphate were by adsorption on to sites produced by metabolism, there should be a large volume within the cells which is freely available to the diffusion of phosphate ions. This volume can be found by determining the degree of dilution of a known addition of phosphate to a thick cell suspension and estimating that fraction of the volume of the suspension accessible to the externally added phosphate. If a phosphate impermeable barrier exists near the surface of the cell, the effective cell volume should be approximately equal to the volume of a close-packed centrifuged pad less 26 per cent., the interspace volume for close-packed spheres (Conway and Downey, 1950). On the other hand, if there is no osmotic barrier or if the barrier is broken down by such reagents as trichloracetic acid or butanol, the effective cell volume should be approximately equal to the specific volume of the cell materials. The phosphate impermeable volume of normal *Staphylococcus* cells in 0·1 M sodium chloride was found to be $2·42 \pm 0·05$ ml. per g. cell dry weight, in tolerably good agreement with the figure of $2·67 \pm 0·01$ ml. per g. for the close-packed volume less 26 per cent. (Mitchell, 1953). After treatment with n-butanol or trichloracetic acid the phosphate impermeable volume decreases to $0·93 \pm 0·09$ ml. per g., which is in good agreement with the apparent specific volume of the solid materials in the cell, namely 0·8 ml. per g. If the inorganic phosphate is bound to cellular constituents from which there is no barrier to the external medium, the concentration to which the phosphate must rise, if it is all outside the impermeable barrier found in *Staphylococcus aureus*, seems to preclude the possibility that phosphate is held in the cell by any unspecific binding. Furthermore, if the exchange-adsorption hypothesis is correct, the so-called inorganic phosphate of the cell would be held on combining groups corresponding in number to acid-soluble inorganic phosphate molecules. The inhibition of the exchange of phosphate on a combining group would not be expected to occur unless the inhibitor molecule were close to the combining group. Hence, unless action at a distance were to be postulated, the number of molecules of an inhibitor required to retard exchange reactions should be of the same order as the number of molecules of acid-soluble inorganic phosphate. Phenyl-Hg$^+$ inhibits exchange at a concentration well below that required for association with any possible exchange-adsorption sites.

The uptake of phosphate by yeast is the same whether measured chemically or by ^{32}P activity. This indicates an absence of exchange of cellular and extracellular phosphate (Goodman and Rothstein, 1957). This is in contrast to the esterification reaction involving 3-phosphoglyceraldehyde. Goodman and Rothstein suggested that an essentially irreversible phosphate transport step is involved, which would account for the lack of exchange to be expected if the extra- and intracellular phosphate were in direct equilibrium. It is more likely that the close connection between phosphate absorption and glycolysis lies in the provision of energy by the latter for the transport process. This linkage may account for the fact that, although glycolysis is essential for phosphate uptake, the coupling is neither obligatory nor stoichometric. Thus glycolytic reactions continue at a normal rate in the absence of extracellular phosphate. The maximal rate of phosphate uptake observed for yeast cells is 260 mM per kg. of cells per hour. Sugar uptake under the same conditions is 1500 mM per kg. of cells per hour. In the absence of phosphate, the rate of sugar uptake is reduced only slightly. Furthermore, a variety of agents can uncouple phosphate absorption from glycolysis. Kamen and Spiegelman (1948) found that azide reduces phosphate uptake while glycolysis is unaffected, and Samson, Katz and Harris (1955) showed that fatty acids reduce the uptake of phosphate by yeast, although under certain conditions they have no effect on the glycolytic rate of the cells.

Potassium ions stimulate still further the high rate of phosphate uptake by yeast induced by the presence of glucose

(Rothstein and Enns, 1946); the same is found for *Eschericha coli* (Roberts and Roberts, 1950). Goodman and Rothstein showed that this effect is complex. In the first instance, the effect is entirely specific for potassium, since sodium cannot stimulate phosphate uptake. The extent of the stimulation is dependent upon pH (Fig. 17). The pH optimum for phosphate uptake shifts from pH 6·5, when no potassium is present, to a pH of 4·8 in the presence of potassium. Although potassium stimulates the fermentation of yeast, this high rate of fermentation is independent of pH. Three explanations were offered for the increase of phosphate uptake by potassium. Firstly, there might be a direct effect of potassium on the transport mechanism. Secondly, a shift of pH in the cell surface region by a membrane hydrolysis phenomenon might make the outer membrane of the cell more permeable. The outer membrane of the cell is impermeable to anions but permeable to potassium and hydrogen ions. Therefore, an increase in the extracellular potassium results in an alkalisation of the cell surface compartment by an exchange reaction. This phenomenon could account for the reversal of the inhibitory effects of hydrogen ions on fermentation (Rothstein and Demis, 1953) and, perhaps also, for the shifts in optima of the pH curves for phosphate uptake. Thirdly, the balance of cellular cations and anions, which can be ensured with the presence of potassium in the medium, may also be a factor accounting for the stimulation of phosphate uptake. Small quantities of phosphate ions can be taken up without cation absorption, at the expense of cellular buffer capacity. However, uptake of phosphate over an extended period can only continue if potassium is also absorbed. However, the uptake of potassium and phosphate is not directly linked. If both ions are presented to the cell at the same time, potassium is taken up more rapidly (Rothstein and Enns, 1946), but, after 10 to 15 minutes, the uptake of the cation slows down and the rates of uptake of the two ions become roughly equal.

It has been shown consistently for all plant cells that the uptake of phosphate decreases from pH 6·0 upwards (Van den Honert, 1933; Harley and McCready, 1950; Mitchell, 1954; Hagen and Hopkins, 1955; Goodman and Rothstein, 1957). The majority of these authors have found that the decrease of phosphate uptake corresponds sufficiently with the change in

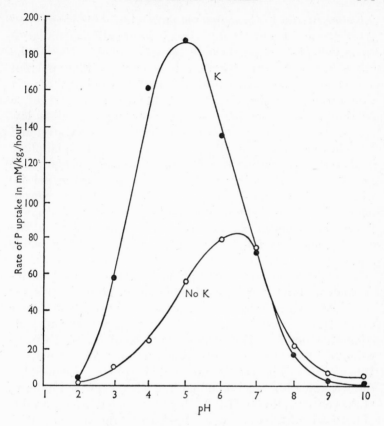

FIG. 17. The effects of pH on the uptake of phosphate in the presence and absence of potassium. Either *cis*-hydroxyamino-methane or triethylamine were used as a buffer mixture with succinic acid. In the pH range of 6·5 to 7·5 in which the buffers are ineffective, the suspensions were continuously titrated with triethylamine or with hydrochloric acid. The yeast concentration was 50 mg. per ml.; glucose, 0·2 M; and potassium, 0·02 M. (Goodman and Rothstein, 1957).

the second dissociation of phosphoric acid to suggest that the monovalent ion H_2PO_4' is absorbed, in complete preference to the bivalent ion HPO_4''. Hagen and Hopkins, who investigated the phosphate uptake by barley roots over a range of external phosphate concentrations containing ^{32}P, concluded from the different rates of uptake over a range of pH from 4 to 8 that there are two sites of phosphate absorption. H_2PO_4' is absorbed through one site and HPO_4'' through another. The data could equally well by explained by the adsorption of phosphate on the glass walls of the containers. Such an effect will be apparent particularly at low concentrations (10^{-6} M) and at those pH values tending to alkalinity. This would mean that the effective concentration of phosphate would be reduced, and at low concentrations such an effect can be considerable (Martin and Russell, 1950). Consequently, as the concentration of phosphate in the external solution is reduced, the quantity of phosphate absorbed as a percentage of the quantity absorbed at pH 4·0 will become very much less. In the absence of a more rigorous demonstration, one can only conclude that the H_2PO_4' ion is the preferred ion in phosphate uptake by plant cells and the contribution of the HPO_4'' ion to such uptake is indeterminable and may be nil.

The actual process of phosphate uptake may well be independent of pH over a considerable range. With *Staphylococcus aureus* (Mitchell, 1954), the dependence of the rate of exchange of ^{32}P upon external concentration at constant pH and ionic strength follows a Michaelis-Menton relationship, giving a value of 1·6 mM for the Michaelis constant (Km) at pH 6·8. When expressed in terms of the total phosphate concentration, the Km value is a function of pH but, when expressed in terms of the concentration of H_2PO_4', it was estimated to have a value of 0·8 ± 0·1 mM, independent of pH over a range from pH 5·5 to 8·5.

The process of phosphate uptake by tissues of higher plants has been much less extensively investigated, when compared with those studies using micro-organisms. Absorption of phosphate occurs in the absence of sugars (Harley and McCready, 1950; Butler, 1953b; Lundegårdh, 1959). Sugars however stimulate phosphate uptake by wheat roots (Butler, 1953b; Stenlid, 1959), but the effect appears to be complicated. Galactose, for instance, causes an increased phosphate uptake by fresh roots, while glucose is only effective after the roots have been stored for several hours in distilled water. Mannose, on the other hand, inhibits the uptake of phosphate by fresh roots, yet stimulates absorption after 24 hours' storage in distilled water. Oxygen uptake is also inhibited and stimulated in a similar manner, but the relation between the two is not strict. D. H. Jennings (unpublished data) found that glucose has no effect on the phosphate uptake by beech mycorrhiza. Lack of stimulation by exogenous sugars is to be anticipated, in view of the presence of respirable sugars in sufficient quantity within higher plant tissues. The lack of any response to sugars provides no evidence of the absence of linkage between cellular metabolism and phosphate uptake. Phosphate uptake by beech mycorrhiza is an oxygen-sensitive process with a high Q_{10} (Harley, McCready and Brierley, 1953, and 1958). DNP and sodium azide (at concentrations which increase respiration) inhibit phosphate uptake by beech mycorrhiza (Harley, McCready, Brierley and Jennings, 1956). Sodium azide in fact causes a loss of phosphate from beech mycorrhizal roots, which is probably similar to the loss of phosphate from beet discs in the presence of DNP observed by Robertson, Wilkins and Weeks (1951). Loss of phosphate can also be observed under anaerobic conditions (Harley and Brierley, 1954), but under normal aerobic conditions phosphate can neither be washed out of the tissue nor does any exchange occur (Harley and Brierley, 1954, and 1955). Phosphate uptake by wheat roots appears to be similarly sensitive to metabolic inhibitors (Butler, 1953b; Stenlid, 1959); however, in wheat roots the phosphate present within the tissue is exchangeable with phosphate in the external medium. Exchangeability of incorporated radioactive phosphate has been found in wheat seedlings (Hevesy, 1946) and barley seedlings (Russell and Martin, 1953), so that the observed exchange phenomena in wheat roots is unlikely to be due to exudation from the cut ends of the roots.

There have been no observations on the effect of potassium on phosphate uptake by excised roots. Chloride, however, reduces phosphate absorption by wheat roots (Lundegårdh, 1959).

The phosphate uptake by micro-organisms, although metabolically controlled, does not appear to be directly related to the known paths of intermediary metabolism within those organisms. The incorporation of phosphate into those cells appears to be by some specific absorption process and not to be the result of simple incorporation into organic compounds. The same may be true for higher plant cells. Nevertheless, very little is known about the pattern of incorporation of phosphate once it is absorbed by such cells. Data of this kind could provide valuable evidence towards establishing the identity of the relationship between metabolic events within the cell and the accumulation of phosphate from the external medium. In principle, such an investigation is extremely simple and follows a similar line to the work on the pathway of carbon in photosynthesis using radioactive carbon dioxide. The object of such a study is the identification of the compound or compounds first labelled with ^{32}P once the phosphate has entered the cell. However, certain difficulties present themselves. Orthophosphate can be extracted from plant cells, and it is conceivable that this compound might be first labelled with ^{32}P. Contamination from the external medium will produce a similar result, though this can be guarded against by careful washing of the cells or tissues involved. The interpretation of results will also be difficult if there are extensive passive fluxes across the cell membranes in addition to any active mechanism which may be present. Extensive passive exchange of labelled ions between the external medium and the cell would obscure the working of such a mechanism. If these difficulties are removed, there still remains the problem of heterogeneity of the tissue. Shaw and Stadie (1957) have shown the presence of two metabolic pathways in the rat diaphragm involving the sugar phosphates, glucose-l-phosphate and glucose-6-phosphate. In one, the conversion of glucose to glycogen is initiated by the transport of glucose to the interior of the cell followed by esterification and polymerisation to glycogen. The phosphate esters formed— namely glucose-l-phosphate and glucose-6-phosphate—remain in the interior of the cell. Hexose diphosphate is not formed from this internal glucose-6-phosphate. Accordingly, no significant lactic acid is formed. The conversion of glucose to lactic acid takes place at some other locus, tentatively assumed to be the surface of the cell. The dissimilation of glucose follows the Embden-Meyerhof pathway. Thus, there appears to be a compartmentalisation of the hexose phosphate esters within the cells of the rat diaphragm. There is evidence of a similar compartmentalisation in yeast. Rothstein, Jennings, Demis and Bruce (1959) isolated a structural unit from yeast by slowly drying the cells, following the drying by lyophilisation. This unit is capable of high rates of fermentation and it accumulates phosphate in a non-exchangeable manner. It produces alcohol and CO_2 but shows no ability to respire; it synthesises very little glycogen. The structural unit is completely impermeable to phosphate esters in either direction. Taking into account the fact that particles have also been isolated from yeast cells which show oxidative phosphorylation (Utter, Keech and Nossal, 1958), it is clear that care must obviously be exercised in the interpretation of data obtained from isotope studies due to compartmentalisation of phosphate compounds within the cells. That such care is in fact needed has been demonstrated by D. H. Jennings (unpublished data), who has shown that there is a small fraction of the orthophosphate in beech mycorrhizal roots which varies in quantity depending on the metabolic state of the root. This pool of orthophosphate is sufficiently small to be undetectable by chemical means but can be distinguished by the use of isotopes. While the major portion of orthophosphate within mycorrhizal roots appears to be metabolically inactive, this small pool is closely connected with the metabolism of the roots and may be intimately associated with the phosphate ions entering the root from the external medium. Such a finding emphasises, still further, the care which is needed in any study devoted to the investigation of the immediate compounds labelled by isotopes once they have entered the cell.

Loughman and Russell (1957) have studied the initial metabolism of phosphate by roots of intact barley plants using ^{32}P. Their results are equivocal for two reasons. There is no evidence that the incorporation of ^{32}P by the roots is the result of a specific transport step. Since it is known that ^{32}P once accumulated is lost from the roots when barley plants are transferred to a phosphate-free medium, it is possible that the observed labelling patterns are due to exchange and that the net uptake of the isotope plays a subsidiary part. Furthermore, Loughman and Russell provide no evidence of the effectiveness of the washing procedure used to remove ^{32}P from the free space of the roots. While they were conerned mainly with the metabolism of phosphate once incorporated within the root, their results are only valuable with regard to an examination of the mechanism responsible for the uptake of phosphate by barley roots when the status of the labelled orthophosphate has been clearly determined. It is possible that the initial high activity in the orthophosphate fraction, which was consistently observed, is in the free space. Provided that this is not the case, it appears that phosphate, when accumulated within barley roots, enters a pool of orthophosphate from which organic compounds become labelled. Apparently the nucleotide pool is closely connected with the orthophosphate pool. D. H. Jennings (unpublished data) has made very similar observations using beech mycorrhizal roots. Special care was given to the washing of roots and to the study of any possible exchange mechanisms. It appears that the phosphate first enters the orthophosphate pool intimately associated with metabolism (which has been mentioned earlier in this section). If this evidence is correct, the mechanism of phosphate uptake is distinct from those metabolic pathways involved in the incorporation of phosphate into organic compounds, a conclusion in agreement with those drawn from the study of phosphate uptake in yeast and *Staphylococcus aureus*.

Nevertheless, this does not preclude the possibility that those processes whereby phosphate is incorporated into various consituents of the cell exert an effect on the primary absorption process. Ketchum (1939) using illuminated cultures of *Nitzeschia closterium* showed that phosphate uptake is increased by increasing the concentrations of nitrate in the medium. D. H. Jennings (unpublished data) has found that ammonium chloride can have a stimulatory effect on phosphate uptake by beech mycorrhizal roots. This increase in phosphate uptake is accompanied by an increase in the quantity of phosphate in all fractions of phosphate within the root. Ketchum made no analyses of the metabolism of the phosphate after absorption, though here too nitrate may increase the incorporation of phosphate into organic compounds. The increased uptake of phosphate could be caused by several factors. There might be a synthesis of a carrier compound responsible for the absorption of phosphate into the cell as a result of the increased availability of nitrogen compounds. In view of the known activity of nitrogen compounds in promoting high rates of metabolism with concomitant synthetic reactions, the effect of ammonium ions is most likely to be due to the more rapid rate of removal of phosphate from the pool of orthophosphate into which the incoming phosphate from the external medium feeds.

CHAPTER 10

THE UPTAKE OF INORGANIC NITROGEN
COMPOUNDS

The decision to treat inorganic nitrogen compounds as one group with respect to their uptake by plant tissues rests with observations showing close interrelationship of nitrate and ammonia uptake. Cramer and Myers (1948) found that ammonia suppresses the uptake of nitrate by algae, and Morton and MacMillan (1954) found the same for mould fungi. El Shishiny (1955) observed the same phenomenon with sweet potato. Not all plant tissues exhibit this phenomenon, for El Shishiny found that the uptake of nitrate by radish root issue is unaffected by the presence of ammonia in the external medium. This phenomenon may account for the various observations in which in one case a plant may show better utilisation of ammonium nitrogen than nitrate nitrogen (pine-apple roots, Sideris, Krauss and Young, 1937; rice plants, Bonner, 1946; potato sprouts, Street, Kenyon and Watson, 1946) or vice versa (barley, Arnon, 1937; oats, Arenz, 1941).

There is always the possibility with weakly dissociated compounds that uptake can involve both the undissociated molecule and the ionic species. The effect of pH on the rate of uptake is often suggestive in this respect. Thus Morton and MacMillan (1954) found that the rate of ammonia uptake by *Scopulariopsis versicolor* is increased with increasing pH, and this led them to suggest that uptake of ammonia is via the un-dissociated molecule. Becking (1956), on the other hand, using intact maize plants, showed that at low ammonium concentrations ammonium uptake is accompanied by an equivalent loss of hydrogen ions from the roots. At higher concentrations of ammonia, the hydrogen ion release is only 75 to 80 per cent. of the ammonium uptake. This can be explained by an increased absorption of anions. Thus, in maize it appears that the ionic species are absorbed, and, in agreement with this hypothesis, Becking found that the rate of ammonia uptake is the same at

K

pH 4·6 as it is at pH 6·0. Furthermore, the relationship of rate of uptake to concentration of ammonia is in the form of a rectangular hyperbola—a similar relationship has been found for other cations.

Although it appears that ammonia enters the cells of *Scopulariopsis* as the undissociated molecule, Morton and MacMillan (1954) gave no evidence as to the mechanism involved. Subsequent investigations (MacMillan, 1956a) showed that ammonia enters the cells of the mould fungi by diffusion of the undissociated molecule. The evidence for this is as follows. In the first instance, the rate of ammonia uptake is independent of the rate at which it is removed by assimilation. Ammonia is rapidly lost into the medium when mycelia, which have been accumulating ammonia, are returned to the ammonia-free buffer. The loss is rapid, 50 per cent. of the ammonia in the mycelium being lost in 15 minutes. Furthermore, if respiratory inhibitors are added, at concentrations which inhibit endogenous respiration and ammonia assimilation, there is very little change in the level of ammonia inside the cells.

If ammonia diffuses into the mycelium as the undissociated molecule, the rate of diffusion will depend on the concentration gradient between the external solution and the interior of the cell. However, the concentration of undissociated molecules will depend upon the degree of dissociation, and this in turn will depend upon the pH of both the external medium and the cell contents. It will also depend upon the buffer capacity of the cell contents. MacMillan measured the ammonia content and internal pH of mycelia kept in a medium of constant ammonia composition but with varying pH. Although she herself questioned the efficacy of the method by which she determined the pH of the cell contents, she found that this pH rises only slowly, as the pH of the external medium rises from 5·0 to 9·0. Calculating the expected internal pH from the observed internal ammonia concentration, she found that there was reasonable agreement between the observed pH and the calculated value, which provides favourable evidence for the diffusion hypothesis.

Nitrate uptake by mould fungi is dependent upon pH (Morton and MacMillan, 1954). The rate of uptake rises from pH 4·0 to a maximum between pH 6·0 and 7·0 and falls at higher pH values. Van den Honert and Hooymans (1955) found that between pH 6·0 and 8·0 the rate of nitrate absorption by maize roots decreases as the pH increases (at pH values lower than 6·0, they obtained variable results). Arnon, Fratzke and Johnson (1942) found little influence of external pH between 4·0 and 9·0 on the nitrate absorption of Bermuda grass, lettuce and tomato, and Weissman (1950) found a similar result with wheat seedlings over the pH range 4·3 to 6·3.

After shaking mycelia of *Scopulariopsis brevicaulis* in phosphate buffer (pH 7·0) containing potassium nitrate, the final level of nitrate in the mycelium varies very much less than the external concentration. At the higher nitrate concentrations, the internal nitrate concentration is similar to the external concentration, but, at the lower concentrations, accumulation of nitrate occurs in the cells (MacMillan, 1956b).

If mycelia which have been accumulating nitrate are transferred to nitrate-free buffer, nitrate is rapidly lost to the medium. Although such mycelia have been accumulating nitrate for 24 hours, within two hours after the transference to a nitrate-free medium, 50 per cent. of the internal nitrate is lost to the external medium.

The uptake of nitrate is increased in the presence of glucose. Under these conditions, the level of nitrate within the mycelia remains at a low level, the major portion of the nitrate entering the mycelia being assimilated. Although this increased assimilation is accompanied by a rise in the rate of respiration, it is not known to what extent the increased rate of respiration is connected with the uptake of nitrate. Respiratory energy does appear to be required for nitrate uptake, for 0·01 M potassium cyanide inhibits the uptake of nitrate by mycelia in a glucose free media. Similar results are obtained with 0·02 M sodium azide.

Attention has been drawn to the fact that ammonia inhibits the uptake of nitrate by *Scopulariopsis brevicaulis* (Morton and MacMillan, 1954). MacMillan (1956b) found that ammonia is only effective in this respect if glucose is also present in the medium. In the absence of glucose, ammonia assimilation only continues for one to two hours, but when glucose is supplied, ammonia assimilation continues, and it appears that nitrate assimilation is inhibited, for under these conditions the nitrate level in the cells, although lower than in the absence of glucose, is much higher than when glucose alone is present in the medium.

Morton (1956) measured the activity of the whole nitrate reducing system (nitratase) in mycelia of mould fungi (either intact or ground). He found that the nitratase activity of mycelia in glucose-nitrate media falls to a very low value within one hour after addition of ammonia and it remains at this value until all added ammonia has been assimilated. This fall in activity appears to depend on the assimilation of ammonia by the mycelium, since it does not occur in conditions when such assimilation is prevented. Furthermore, ammonia itself has no effect on the test system (mycelia, intact or ground, in the presence of 0.2 M sodium fluoride). The nitratase activity is also found to depend on the presence of assimilable carbohydrate, falling rapidly in its absence to a very low value. It appears that the loss of nitratase activity during the assimilation of ammonia and in the absence of carbohydrate is primarily due to a loss of nitrate reductase activity.

There is no explanation as to the mechanism whereby ammonia brings about this loss of nitrate reductase activity. Morton claims that the observed changes in nitratase activity correspond to the physiological facts previously observed (Morton and MacMillan, 1954) and account for the blocking of nitrate, but not of nitrite, uptake in the presence of ammonium ions. However, when the data of MacMillan (1956b) is taken into consideration, it is clear that this is not so. If reduction of nitrate were involved in its uptake, one would not expect to extract nitrate from the mycelia. Nor would one expect nitrate uptake to occur in the absence of glucose, since nitrate reductase activity is reduced equally under these conditions. Furthermore, the loss of nitrate reductase, although highly significant, is rarely complete. It is probable that ammonia prevents nitrate assimilation by inactivation of the nitratase activity, but ammonia must also exert an (as yet undefined) effect upon nitrate uptake, for otherwise one cannot explain the low concentration of nitrate ions in the mycelia in the presence of glucose and ammonia. Since nitrite uptake is unaffected, the action of ammonia cannot be through unspecific ion effects but it must be through a much more specific mechanism.

CHAPTER 11

UPTAKE OF ANIONS OTHER THAN PHOSPHATE AND NITRATE

Chloride and bromide ions are the classical anions used in the study of salt uptake by plant cells. The choice of these ions has been governed by the ease with which they can be estimated, the great importance of the chloride ion in the ionic environment of marine plant cells and cells from brackish water and the fact that the ions when absorbed appear to be metabolically inactive within the cell. Many studies using these ions have been concerned not so much with the actual uptake process but with the relationship between salt absorption and metabolism. In these instances, the halide ions have been used more because they provide a convenient measure of the salt absorbed rather than because of a direct interest in the uptake of these ions *per se*. Consequently, little is known in detail about the kinetics of halide entry into plant cells.

There are a number of isolated facts about chloride and bromide uptake. Epstein (1953) found that chloride ions competitively interfere with the uptake of bromide ions by excised barley roots. Nitrate at a similar concentration to the concentration of bromide ions, has little effect on the uptake of these latter ions. Lundegårdh (1959) on the other hand, observed that potassium nitrate inhibits the uptake of chloride ions by potato tissue. He also observed that chloride uptake from 0·005 M potassium chloride is increased by about 100 per cent. by 0·05 M potassium phosphate and by about 50 per cent. by 0·05 M potassium sulphate. Hurd (1959) found that bicarbonate ions appear to stimulate the uptake of chloride ions by discs of red beet. There is also, of course, the important fact that chloride ions are actively transported into large algal cells, the transport step being located at the tonoplast (see chapter 3).

The problem of iodine accumulation in seaweeds is related to such studies concerned with the uptake of chloride and bromide ions, for it is important to know whether or not iodide ions are the species involved in the absorption process. Considering the theoretical aspects of the problem, it would indeed be interesting if the iodide ions were involved, for, in view of the observations made by Epstein that chloride and bromide compete for the same absorption mechanism in barley roots, one might expect that the large concentration of chloride ions in sea water would prevent iodine from being absorbed by seaweeds as the iodide ion.

Klemperer (1957) suggested, from data obtained with *Fucus ceranoides*, that iodine accumulation in this seaweed is indeed brought about by uptake of the iodide ion. He suggested that there is a specific acceptor which combines reversibly with iodide ion and transports the ion across a boundary in the cell to be accumulated within cells in a bound form. The evidence for this is as follows. The uptake of a certain proportion of the total ^{131}I corresponds to the uptake of the same proportion of the iodide in the medium. The initial rate of uptake of iodide varies with the external concentration over the range 1 to 20 μM, as if iodide uptake depended on a reversible combination with a site in the tissue. In agreement with this, the presence of added carrier iodide reduces the rate of uptake of [131]I.

This is the most stisfactory evidence in favour of iodine being accumulated in *Fucus ceranoides* as the result of the absorption of iodide ions. Klemperer gives other data relating to the problem. The rate of uptake of ^{131}I is diminished by approximately 50 per cent. as a result of incubation at 0° or in the presence of 100 mM cyanide, 10 mM DNP or 50 μM p-chloromercuribenzoate. Respiration is inhibited by cyanide, increased by DNP and unaffected by p-chloromercuribenzoate. Perchlorate, thiocyanate and nitrate act as competitive inhibitors of uptake of iodide. At high concentrations, perchlorate releases small amounts of ^{131}I from the tissue. Thiocyanate releases larger amounts, but, in both cases, this effect is diminished when added carrier iodide is present.

Shaw (1959) has presented evidence that the accumulation of iodine by *Laminaria digitata* is through the uptake of the hydrolysis product of iodine, HIO, and that the iodide ion is not absorbed. [131]I absorption is slowed or halted by thiocyanate, thiosulphate, metabisulphite, catechol, tyrosine and pyruvate at concentrations of 1 to 3 × 10⁻³ M. The full effect of these inhibitors persists only for so long as they are present in the sea water surrounding the weed. These inhibitors all react with iodine in some manner. Thiocyanate, thiosulphate and metabisulphite react rapidly with iodine to give iodide; catechol, a powerful reducing agent, probably reacts in the same way. Pyruvate, on the other hand, combines with iodine to give iodoform, whilst tyrosine is iodinated by alkaline iodine solutions. This suggests that uptake in some way depends upon the iodine molecule.

When iodide is added to sea water associated with brown weeds, there is a rapid liberation of iodine. This process has been extensively studied by Dangeard (1928a, 1928b and 1930), who termed it iodovolatilisation and noted that it required oxygen. In agreement with this, Shaw found that iodine is not liberated from externally supplied iodide when *Laminaria* is in anaerobic conditions. The same atmosphere halts the ¹³¹I uptake from sea water containing 10⁻⁴ M iodide, an observation in agreement with the concept that the presence of iodine is essential for uptake, for under these conditions the weed is unable to oxidise added iodide. When, however, the sea water containing added iodide is replaced by sea water containing iodine, ¹³¹I is rapidly taken into the tissues even when anaerobic conditions are still present.

Calculations of the partitioning of iodine between the various forms I′, HIO and I₃′ show that, as the total iodine concentration increases, the contribution of HIO to the equilibrium mixture diminishes. Comparison of ¹³¹I uptake over a range of iodine concentrations shows the uptake rate is proportional to the calculated percentage of iodine as HIO (Fig. 18). Shaw suggested that, in the absence of contrary evidence, the most satisfactory conclusion is the simplest hypothesis consistent with the facts, namely that HIO is the form of iodine which penetrates the weed. Shaw did point out that it is possible that a compound formed from HIO facilitates the uptake of iodine in some other form.

This hypothesis provides a more satisfactory explanation of the data obtained by Klemperer, especially the results obtained with thiocyanate. The finding that the uptake of ¹³¹I decreases with an increase in the external iodine concentration is also in

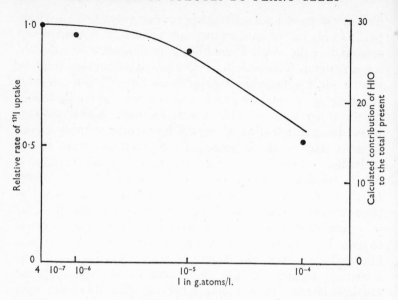

FIG. 18. The relative rates of ^{131}I uptake from sea water (pH 8·0) containing various concentrations of added iodide. The rates are stated in relation to the uptake from sea water containing its natural concentration of iodine (taken as 4×10^{-7} g. atoms per l.). The continuous line is based on the reaction:

$$\tfrac{1}{2}O_{2(g)} + 2I'_{(aq.)} + 2H^+_{(aq.)} = I_{2(aq.)} + H_2O_{(l.)}$$

and on the following assumptions:

(1) that near the weed surface in iodide-oxidase brings I', I_2, O_2, H_2O and H^+ into equilibrium.

(2) that the chemical reactions are rapid compared with the rate of removal of iodine from the surface.

(3) that IO_3' formation is negligible over the short periods involved in the experiments.

The computations have been made for dilute solutions at a pH of 8·0, oxygen partial pressure of 0·21 atm. and 25°. The continuous line shows the calculated contribution that HIO makes towards the total iodine contribution. Scaling between left and right is arbitrarily adjusted to give agreement at one point (4×10^{-7} g. atoms per l.). (Shaw, 1959.)

harmony with this hypothesis. Presumably those other compounds which inhibit the uptake of ^{131}I by *Fucus ceranoides*, cyanide, dinitrophenol and p-chloromercuribenzoate, interfere with the oxidative metabolism of the frond.

There is good evidence that selenate competitively interferes with the absorption of sulphate by a variety of plant cells, and that the uptake of these two ions is by the same mechanism. Shrift (1954) observed that selenate decreases the rate of growth of *Chlorella vulagaris*, and that this effect is prevented by the addition of sulphate to the medium. Sulphate also reduces the absorption of selenate. Weissman and Trelease (1955) found that the growth of *Aspergillus niger* is related to the sulphate/selenate ratio in the external medium. As this ratio increases, growth increases and selenate uptake diminishes. Selenate uptake is also reduced by addition of organic sulphur compounds in solution, probably as a result of the inhibition of selenate metabolism within the cell, for it is found that the percentage of the total selenium within the mycelia found in the inorganic form increases in the presence of methionine. Leggett and Epstein (1956) using excised barley roots showed that selenate competitively inhibits the uptake of sulphate, while chloride, nitrate and phosphate have no measurable effect. The evidence from these three different organisms shows once again the possible presence of a specific absorption mechanism for compounds of similar chemical identity.

CHAPTER 12

AMINO ACID UPTAKE

There is a surprising paucity of references in the literature to the uptake of these compounds from the external medium by plant cells, considering the acknowledged importance of amino acids in nitrogen metabolism. No doubt the emphasis in botany on the autotrophic nutrition of green plants has contributed to this lack of interest, for such emphasis on inorganic nutrition has meant that the absorption of nitrogen compounds has been considered only in terms of nitrates, nitrites and ammonium salts. This emphasis is both mistaken and unfortunate. It is unlikely under natural conditions that inorganic nitrogen compounds are the sole source of nitrogen for growing plants. Within the soil or any other natural medium for plant growth, a whole range of nitrogen compounds, both organic and inorganic, must be available in solution. The fact that plants are essentially autotrophic in their metabolism does not put any premium on inorganic salts as a nutrient supply for plant cells and tissues. There is no *a priori* reason why organic nitrogen compounds should not be equally effective, and, from the limited number of studies with higher plant tissues (El Shishiny, 1955; El Shishiny and Nosser, 1957a and b; Birt and Hird, 1958a; Reinhold and Powell, 1958), it is obvious that amino acids can be readily absorbed by such tissues and rapidly metabolised once they are absorbed. For those interested in the relationship between the internal environment of living cells and the surrounding external environment, amino acids are an instructive class of compounds, for they possess many interesting properties. In the first instance, they provide a series of organic compounds which exist in ionic form. Secondly, their function inside many cells is often well known and well defined. Thirdly, their ability to exist in isomeric forms provides a valuable method of examining a concept, which, although never annunciated, has had lip-service paid to it by many workers, namely that uptake processes are closely analogous to enzymic reactions.

It is well known that enzymes are invariably stereoisomerically specific in their action. If the mechanism responsible for the uptake of amino acids were of an enzymic nature, then a similar specificity would be expected.

Bacteria

Gale and his co-workers found that certain gram-positive bacteria contain high concentrations of free amino acids inside their cells (Gale, 1947; Taylor, 1947). Originally, they suggested that the accumulation of free amino acids distinguished gram-positive bacteria from gram-negative bacteria. This suggestion now appears to be unfounded, and the inability of Taylor to find free amino acids within gram-negative bacterial cells appears to be due to the very much greater ability of gram-positive cells to effect a higher concentration of amino acids within their cells and the greater facility with which amino acids leave the cells of gram-negative bacteria when they are washed in water (Gale and McQuillen, 1957). Gale and his co-workers were essentially interested in those factors responsible for the accumulation of amino acids within the cells of *Streptococcus faecalis* and *Staphylococcus aureus*. While they were interested in the actual absorption processes, the bulk of their measurements was made with a view to following the changes in the internal concentration of amino acids. Most of their studies were concerned with the accumulation of glutamic acid. This acid was chosen because it could be assayed readily by the specific glutamic decarboxylase preparation of Gale (1945).

Gale, using cells which contained little free amino acid, showed that there is no uptake of glutamic acid by *Streptococcus faecalis* at 0° or at 37° in the absence of glucose. In the presence of glucose, glutamic acid accumulates within the cell, and the $Q_{10_{20°-30°}}$ for this process is 1·94. The effect of pH on the uptake of glutamic acid is essentially a reflexion of the effect of pH on glucose fermentation. Uptake is against a concentration gradient, which appears to be constant over the range of concentrations studied; while the effect of the external concentration on the rate of uptake is very similar to the dependence of the rate of an enzyme reaction on the concentration of substrate. The uptake of glutamic acid by *Staphylococcus aureus* is similarly dependent on glucose metabolism and temperature.

With *Streptococcus faecalis* there is no loss of glutamic acid from the cell into distilled water or into a solution containing salts of phosphate and chloride. Glutamic acid is however lost in the presence of 1 per cent. glucose (Gale, 1947). On the other hand, when cells of *Staphylococcis aureus* are incubated in the same buffered salt solution, there is a slow loss of glutamic acid from the cells (Gale, 1951). Such differences of behaviour may explain the observed differences of response by the two organisms to metabolic inhibitors. Over the range 10^{-5} M to 10^{-3} M, DNP produces a marked increase in the free glutamic acid inside the cells of *Streptococcus*. In contrast, the accumulation of glutamic acid in cells of *Staphylococcus* is extremely sensitive to DNP at the same concentrations. The process of accumulation of glutamic acid is 20 to 100 times more sensitive to DNP than fermentation. At 10^{-2} M DNP complete inhibition of glutamic acid accumulation takes place, yet fermentation is only inhibited by 10 per cent. Sodium azide is effective in a similar manner, although the process of accumulation is not quite so sensitive to this inhibitor as it is to DNP. In the presence of sodium azide, over the range of 10^{-6} M to 10^{-4} M, there is a drop in the concentration of glutamic acid accumulated in the cells of *Streptococcus faecalis*. Above this concentration, there is a marked rise in the glutamic acid which is accumulated inside the cells.

The above data may be explained by postulating that the rate of accumulation of glutamic acid within the cells of *Streptococcus faecalis* and *Staphylococcus aureus* is determined by the rate of efflux of glutamic acid from the cell as well as the rate of influx of the amino acid. It can be postulated that the efflux of glutamic acid from *Streptococcus* is a strictly metabolic process, while the efflux from *Staphylococcus aureus* is a diffusion process which can be arrested by metabolism. It is possible that DNP and azide inhibit this metabolic brake on efflux, so that any glutamic acid taken into the cell cannot accumulate. On the other hand, in *Streptococcus* DNP and azide appear to have their effect on the metabolism of the glutamic acid which is accumulated rather than to affect either the influx or efflux mechanisms. The effect of DNP and sodium azide is similar to that produced by crystal violet and other dyes of the triphenylamine series. It seems unreasonable to conclude that inhibitors act upon the process of influx only in one organism, when there is nothing to prove that the same mechanism is not responsible for influx in both organisms. Such an explanation serves to emphasise the fact that, as with alkali cations, efflux mechanisms may be as important as those responsible for influx in controlling the rate of accumulation of any compound.

The accumulation of glutamic acid in cells of both *Streptococcus faecalis* and *Staphylococcus aureus* is accompanied by the uptake of an equivalent quantity of potassium ions. When sodium are the exclusive cations in the external solution, these ions can replace potassium ions. Potassium ions cannot be replaced by calcium, magnesium or ammonium ions (Davies, Folkes, Gale and Biggar, 1953).

The presence of other amino acids in the external medium can affect the accumulation of glutamic acid within the cells of *Staphylococcus aureus* (Gale, 1951). If a complete mixture of natural amino acids is added to the external medium, the accumulation of free glutamic acid within the cells ceases, and glutamic acid becomes incorporated into cellular material. Accompanying this incorporation, there is a decreased rate of uptake of glutamic acid from the external medium. Gale and Van Halteren (1951) investigated the effect of individual amino acids upon the uptake, subsequent accumulation and metabolism of glutamic acid by *Staphylococcus* cells. They found that amino acids can be placed into three groups according to the effect that they have upon glutamic acid accumulation; that is whether they cause a decrease or an increase or have no effect at all on the rate of accumulation of free glutamic acid within *Staphylococcus* cells.

Of the amino acids which decrease the rate of free glutamic accumulation, aspartic acid is different from the others within the group in its mode of action. The inhibition of glutamic acid accumulation by aspartic acid is determined by the ratio of the two acids and not by the absolute concentration of either. The effect of the addition of aspartic acid is to reduce, by approximately the same amount, the rate of removal of free glutamic acid from the external medium, the rate of accumulation of free glutamic acid within the cells and the rate of disappearance of glutamic acid within the cells. There is no significant appearance of combined glutamate in the supernatant medium or increase in the combined glutamate in the cells. Further, glutamic acid inhibits the accumulation of aspartic acid. All these facts point to the direct competition between aspartic acid and glutamic acid for the sites of uptake. This is highly likely from the similar chemical structure of the two compounds.

On the other hand, the reduction in the rate of free accumulation of glutamic acid by the amino acids alanine, cysteine and glycine is due to a reduction in the effective concentration of glutamic acid in the external medium through the formation of extracellular peptides. These acids inhibit the rate of accumulation but do not decrease the final internal concentration. The formation of extracellular peptides depends upon the presence of glucose. Many of the peptides which are formed are able to penetrate the cell and give rise to free glutamic acid in the cell interior. Some peptides are able to penetrate the cell and give rise to free glutamic acid at a rate very much faster than glutamic acid itself, and this probably accounts for the increased rate of glutamic acid accumulation within the *Staphylococcus* cells, when such cells are suspended in a medium containing leucine or valine together with glutamic acid. There is a highly significant correlation between the rate of accumulation and the product of the partition coefficient between n-butanol and water and the rate of hydrolysis of the peptide by a broken cell preparation (Rowland, Folkes, Gale and Marrion, 1957). Glucose is necessary for the accumulation of glutamic acid, when cells are incubated in the presence of peptides formed between glutamic acid and alanine, glycine, leucine, valine and glutamic acid itself. The rate of accumulation of glutamic acid from α-L-glutamyl-L-glutamic acid and α-L-glutamyl-L-valine possesses the same sensitivity to inhibitors as does the rate of accumulation of glutamic acid within the cells from glutamic acid in the external medium. As there is no evidence to show that the rate of hydrolysis of the peptides is determined by the metabolism of glucose, one can conclude that the uptake of these peptides is determined by metabolic factors in a similar manner to the uptake of glutamic acid itself, though it appears from partition coefficients that other factors may be operative in determining the absolute rate of uptake.

Parallel studies using *Lactobacillus casei* suggest that there are independent mechanisms for the uptake of individual amino acids and for peptides containing the same amino acid. Kihara and Snell (1952) postulated that absorption of peptides containing L-alanine is by a different pathway from that of L-alanine. They based their postulate on the fact that D-alanine antagonises the utilisation of externally supplied L-alanine during growth of vitamin B_6-deficient medium but does not antagonise the utilisation of L-alanine supplied externally in the form of peptides or L-alanine synthesised internally in the presence of vitamin B_6. Leach and Snell (1959) showed that the same appeared to be true for L-glycine and peptides containing L-glycine, for unlabelled glycine has no effect on either the extent or rate of accumulation of radioactivity from the labelled peptide, though no evidence was given to show that the peptides have no effect upon the accumulation of the free amino acid.

In the presence of a complete and balanced mixture of amino acids, there is an increased quantity of combined glutamic acid within the cells. A fall in the free glutamic acid concentration within the cells accompanies this increase of combined glutamic acid. (Gale, 1951). From other data, it appears that the concentration of free glutamic acid within the cells is determined by the balance between the rate at which the acid enters the cell and the rate at which it is metabolised. Therefore this decrease in the rate of accumulation should not be accompanied by a decreased rate of uptake. The inhibition of uptake, which does in fact occur in the presence of a complete and balanced mixture of amino acids, is likely to be due to a variety of causes. Two possibilities are the formation of extracellular peptides in the manner described above and the direct inhibition of uptake by amino acids such as aspartic acid. Gale (1951) suggested that the passage of glutamic acid into the cell involves a metabolic stage which is also part of the process of peptide bond formation, so that glutamic acid does not accumulate in the free state within the cell when the presence of other amino acids renders peptide bond formation possible. It is hard to see how such a process can actually result in a reduced rate of uptake.

While Gale and his co-workers have shown that glutamic acid does not accumulate in streptococcal cells unless glucose is present, Mitchell and Moyle (1956) showed that glutamic acid is prevented from penetrating all but 20 per cent. of the cell when glucose is absent from the medium. The glutamic acid is separated from the interior of the cell by an osmotic barrier and can only be transferred across this barrier through the mediation of metabolic reactions within the cell. With lysine, the situation appears to be different. There is a very rapid equilibration of lysine between the cell interior and the external solution, the rate of this equilibration depending upon the external concentration of lysine. The Q_{10} of the process is low (1·47), and the uptake is not affected by 0·01 M hydrogen cyanide or iodoacetate. The uptake of lysine is increased by pH up to 9·5 (Gale, 1947). Although the above evidence suggests that lysine enters the cell by diffusion, it does so against a concentration gradient. It is also of great interest that the cells are prevented from absorbing lysine by the presence of glucose but are protected from this inactivation by the simultaneous or previous assimilation of glutamic acid. Furthermore, lysine is lost from the cell in the presence of glucose.

The situation is further complicated by the fact that the absorption of lysine by *Streptococcus* cells is inhibited by phosphate in the medium (Najjar and Gale, 1950). At the pH used in the experiments, it is known that *Streptococcus* cells are impermeable to phosphate; nor do any phosphate compounds leak out of the cell. On the other hand, when cells containing a high internal concentration of lysine are suspended in 0·15 M di-sodium hydrogen phosphate, the loss of lysine, which takes place in an equivalent concentration of sodium chloride, is prevented at 4°. At 37°, phosphate is ineffective. However, if the cells have taken up acidic or basic amino acids, no lysine is lost. These amino acids have no protective effect if chloride replaces phosphate. Neutral acids are not effective, even if phosphate is in the medium. Similarly, they have no effect on lysine uptake; whereas basic and acidic amino acids retard lysine uptake, acidic amino acids being the most effective.

Gale and Najjar suggested that the observed phenomena are part of a complex Donnan equilibrium, with phosphate forming one of the non-mobile ions within the cell and lysine (as the isoelectric ion) the mobile ion. They admit that such a hypothesis does not cover all the established facts. It is undoubted that the above phenomena are purely physical in nature. The low-temperature coefficient of lysine uptake and its independence from glucose metabolism clearly points to lysine uptake being under the influence of physical factors.

It is difficult to see how one can arrive at a convincing explanation of lysine uptake from only the above data. Certain factors should be borne in mind. Gale (1947) suggested that lysine passes most easily into the cell in the isoelectric form. While this is possible, it is also conceivable that lysine diffuses into the cell as the purely acidic ion. pI* for lysine is 9·4 while pK_3 is 10·5. There is no data to show the rate of uptake at a pH above 9·5, so that, at present, one cannot decide the species involved in the uptake of lysine. Uptake of the undissociated molecule is typical of many weak acids and bases (Simon and Beevers, 1953), and, should the uptake be through the diffusion of such a molecule, the amount accumulated by the cell will depend on the equilibrium between ion and undissociated molecule, both in the internal environment of the cell and the external medium. The equilibrium within the cell will be governed by the internal pH and the buffer capacity of the cell contents. How far we can think of the absorption of the isoelectric form in these terms remains to be seen.

A complete picture of the events taking place when lysine moves from the external medium into the bacterial cell and vice versa can only be obtained when a knowledge of parallel ion fluxes are known. Lysine, with its isoelectric point of high pH, must be considered in the dissociated form as a base for the data just described, therefore, under the same conditions, movements of cations must be important in determining the quantity of lysine absorbed.

Higher plants

When the uptake of amino acids by higher plant cells is considered, movement into the free space must be taken into account. Birt and Hird (1958b) showed that the initial rate of uptake of amino acids is greatest for those with a high pH value for the isoelectric point. Furthermore, in the presence of 0·1 mM DNP, amino acids can be divided into three groups on the

---

* pI = pH at the isoelectric point.

L

basis of their behaviour with carrot root tissues. DNP has no effect on the initial rate of uptake of those acids with a net positive charge but reduces the rate of uptake thereafter to a very low value; whereas the initial rate of uptake of those acids with a net negative charge is reduced virutally to zero, as is any subsequent uptake. Those acids which have no net charge show a much reduced but slow continuing rate of uptake in the presence of DNP. Assuming that DNP inhibits uptake into the cytoplasm, the DNP insensitive absorption must be diffusion into the free space. It has been pointed out previously that only those ions with a positive charge will be able to diffuse with any facility into the Donnan component of the free space. Consequently, the greater initial rate of uptake of those amino acids with a net positive charge is to be expected. Potassium ions reduce this high initial rate of uptake in agreement with previous knowledge of the properties of the Donnan space (Birt and Hird, 1956).

If the various data for the uptake of amino acids into higher plant cells are examined, there is very little direct evidence which relates uptake to metabolism. Birt and Hird (1956) found that L-histidine is accumulated by carrot slices against a marked concentration gradient, and that this accumulation can be reduced to near zero in the presence of 0.1 mM DNP, 10^{-3} M sodium cyanide being similarly effective. The accumulation of L-histidine clearly depends upon the metabolism of the tissue. On the other hand, Reinhold and Powell (1958) suggested that uptake of glutamic acid by tissues of *Helianthus annuus* is mainly by diffusion, and that the rates of diffusion into the cell and consumption of glutamic acid within the cell are such that diffusion equilibrium with the external solution is not normally established. Depression of uptake under anaerobic conditions can be ascribed to a reduction of the consuming process so that an equilibrium between the glutamic acid inside the cell and the external solution is established. The situation is made more interesting by the observation that indole-3-acetic acid (IAA) stimulates the uptake of glutamic acid by *Helianthus* tissue. Reinhold and Powell suggested that IAA brings about a lessening of the diffusion resistance to glutamic acid. This assumes that glutamic acid is taken up by *Helianthus* cells by the same mechanism in the presence of IAA as in the absence of the auxin. Under anaerobic conditions, the uptake of glutamic acid in the presence of IAA is the same as the uptake of the amino acid from an auxin-free medium, suggesting that the increased uptake in the presence of IAA is metabolically controlled. It is interesting to note that the Q_{10} of the glutamic acid uptake over and above the uptake in the absence of IAA is 1·7, a value more characteristic of metabolic reactions. Reinhold and Powell showed that, in the presence of IAA, glutamic acid forms a larger proportion of the substrate respired. Metabolism of the tissue is therefore changed in the presence of IAA. The glutamic acid absorbed under these conditions may enter the tissue at a different location than that entering by diffusion and be metabolised immediately on entry into the tissue. This would account for the identical glutamic acid content of auxin-treated and untreated tissue. It is possible the glutamic acid absorbed under the influence of auxin is intimately associated with the movements of other ions. Ion exchanges certainly do occur in the presence of IAA. Reinhold (1958) showed the loss of ammonia from etiolated hypocotyls of *Helianthus annuus* is increased in a remarkable manner by IAA. Similarly, Higinbotham, Latimer and Eppley (1953) using several organisms showed a stimulation of rubidium absorption by IAA.

Birt and Hird (1956 and 1958b) have provided very interesting data concerning the uptake of D-amino acids and the interference of the uptake of one amino acid by the presence of another. D-histidine is absorbed by carrot slices at a slower rate than L-histidine. Nevertheless, the former amino acid is absorbed against a concentration gradient (this is absorption into the cell after uptake into the free space has been allowed for). DNP reduces the uptake of D-histidine in the same way as the inhibitor reduces the uptake of L-histidine. It appears that the uptake of D-histidine into the cells of carrot tissues is mediated through metabolic channels in a similar way to the L-isomer. D-alanine and D-phenylalanine are also accumulated inside the cells against a concentration gradient. However, whereas at least 90 per cent. of the L- and D-histidine taken into the tissues can be recovered and whereas a similar percentage of D-alanine and D-phenylalanine can also be recovered, only a much smaller proportion of the L-isomers of these acids can be recovered. The inability to recover these acids in the quantity in which they have been lost from the medium is due to their metabolism in the tissue during the experimental period. Metabolism was demonstrated by the use of labelled amino acids, and the amino acids which are metabolised characteristically induce the biggest rise in oxygen uptake when they are presented to the carrot tissue. Thus, while only L-aspartic and L-glutamic acids, L-alanine and L-phenylalanine of the L-amino acids which were tested are metabolised, none of the D-amino acids which were tested appear to be metabolised, for within the limits of experimental error they were all fully recoverable from the tissue. El-Shishiny and Nosser (1957) found that, while L-aspartate and glutamate are metabolised by carrot root discs, the D-isomers, although absorbed, are metabolically inert, though they do depress the stimulatory effect of the L-isomers on ammonium uptake and metabolism. It is obvious that, whereas D-amino acids are not metabolised within the tissue, they are absorbed into the cell with a great deal of facility. The lack of metabolism of the D-isomers is to be expected from the strong specificity of most enzymes for the L-isomers of amino acids. On the other hand, if an active mechanism were found to be responsible for the marked accumulation of the D-isomers within carrot tissue, then serious doubt would be cast upon the 'enzyme-carrier' hypothesis in this instance.

Birt and Hird (1958b) also studied the competition between various amino acids. Several interesting facts emerge from the study, but there is no coherent picture. L-alanine, L-isoleucine, L-leucine and L-phenylalanine mutually interact with L-histidine. L-methionine reduces the uptake of L-histidine to zero, though L-histidine has no effect on the uptake of L-methionine. On the other hand, L-histidine reduces the uptake of L-aspartic acid, although there is no reverse effect. Similarly, the D-isomers of isoleucine, leucine and phenylalanine, although markedly inhibited in their uptake by L-histidine, did not themselves greatly reduce its uptake. D-isoleucine, D-leucine, D-methionine and D-phenylalanine all inhibit the uptake of D-histidine. However, D-histidine either does not alter the uptake of the competing acid (D-isoleucine, D-phenylalanine) or increases it greatly (D-leucine, D-methionine). For any particular sample of tissue and an amino acid concentration of 5 mM, the total amount of L-amino acid taken up (all results corrected for free space uptake) from the mixtures used is approximately the same, with the exception of that for the system containing L-methionine.

CHAPTER 13

UPTAKE OF SUGARS

Yeast

In the chapter concerned with the free space of plant cells, the work of Rothstein and his co-workers was discussed in relation to the identity of the non-mobile anions of the free space. However, the significance of this work is two-fold, for the experimental results also provide a basis for the most detailed picture for any plant cell of the factors involved in the uptake of glucose. Briefly, the facts already discussed show that there are two species of sites, located near the surface of the yeast cell, which are concerned with the uptake of glucose. The first is inhibited by low concentrations of uranyl ions, while the second only becomes sensitive at higher concentrations of the same ion. The former sites are associated with the fermentation of glucose, while the latter sites are associated with the aerobic metabolism of glucose, through pathways other than those of fermentation. The chemical nature of the sites associated with the uptake of glucose by yeast cells has already been discussed. There now remains the presentation of further facts which extend and clarify the specific problems of hexose sugar absorption by yeast cells.

Fructose and mannose uptake are associated with the same sites (Rothstein, Meier and Hurwitz, 1951). Yeast does not normally ferment galactose, but pre-exposure of the cells to galactose plus glucose results in the appearance of 'adaptive fermentation' of galactose. The fermentation of galactose by adapted cells' is more sensitive, by a factor of about two, to inhibition by uranium than is the fermentation of glucose. It appears that fewer sites are associated with galactose uptake than with glucose uptake.

The surface nature of the sites associated with the uptake of glucose has been emphasised. In view of this, it would be expected that changes in the pH of the external solution would influence the rate of glucose utilisation by the yeast cell. It is necessary, when making the requisite observations, to use inert buffer systems. Potassium counteracts the depressant effects of hydrogen ions on fermentation, with the result that, in the presence of high potassium concentrations, the rate of fermentation is apparently independent of pH over a wide range. Using inert buffer such as triethylamine-succinate-tartarate for the pH range 2·0 to 6·0 and tris-hydroxymethylaminomethane for the range 8·0 to 10·0, Rothstein and Demis (1953) found that the rate of glucose removal from the external medium follows a biphasic curve with optima at about pH 5·0 and pH 8·0. On this basis it appears that there are two different surface sites associated with the uptake of glucose, each responsible for a portion of the pH range. Other evidence for this has been found. At pH 8·5, mannose is respired 55 per cent. as rapidly as glucose, whereas at pH 3·5, mannose is respired 92 per cent. as rapidly. At pH 8·5, glucose uptake is inhibited by calcium, but, at pH 2·0 to 6·0, glucose uptake is markedly increased by calcium.

It is possible that the surface site associated with the uptake of glucose over the alkaline pH range is the hexokinase crystallised by Berger, Slein, Colowick and Cori (1946) and Kunitz and McDonald (1946). It has many similar properties in that it has a pH optimum on the alkaline side, it is only half as active towards mannose as towards glucose and it is inhibited by calcium. This enzyme could not account for the uptake in acid solution. Hurwitz (1953) showed that crystalline hexokinase extracted from yeast has a low activity at pH 5·0, less than 10 per cent. of that at pH 8·0, and there is no measurable activity below 4·0. It seems possible that a second hexokinase, with an acid pH optimum, may be responsible for uptake of glucose at low pH in living cells.

While the glucose uptake system acting in alkaline pH range shows several of the properties of extracted hexokinase, any conclusion about this point can only be attempted after a detailed comparison between extracted hexokinase and the mechanism responsible for glucose absorption. There may indeed be difficulties in such a comparison; Siekevitz (1959) has shown that the activity of hexokinase is markedly enhanced when the enzyme is closely associated with rat liver mitochondria. If hexokinase is added to a medium containing mitochondria and the mitochondria separated from the medium by centrifugation, the activity of the hexokinase associated with the mitochondria is as much as ten times that in the absence of particles. This means that, while a detailed comparison between the enzyme and the uptake system is necessary, interpretation of the results may prove to be difficult, since the activity of the enzyme may be greatly altered by its extraction from the cell.

Rothstein, Jennings, Demis and Bruce (1959) produced a structural unit from yeast which could ferment glucose but could not utilise sugar phosphates. Studies with radioactive tracers clearly showed that sugar phosphates and other glycolytic intermediates are involved in the metabolism of the preparation. When the preparation ferments glucose in the presence of inorganic phosphate, it absorbs phosphate, which is then incorporated into phosphorylated intermediates. None of the phosphate compounds formed can diffuse out of the fermentative structure, nor do internal phosphate esters labelled with ^{32}P exchange their radioactivity with unlabelled compounds in the external medium. There is no evidence concerning the permeability of the living yeast cell to phosphate esters in the external medium. Phosphatases at the surface of the yeast cell prevent this point from being investigated, since the interpretation of any data would be obscured by hydrolysis of the phosphate esters. However, Rothstein *et al.* provided good evidence that their preparation from yeast comes from the peripheral region of the cell, and, in consequence, the incorporation of glucose into the preparation is related to glucose uptake in the intact cell. It is then likely that the intact cell shows a similar impermeability to phosphate esters. This means that, if hexokinase is involved in the uptake of glucose, there still remains the problems of how the glucose phosphate formed is retained within an impermeable barrier. On the other hand, none of the evidence so far put forward removes the possibility that a specific transport step is involved, which is independent of the reaction of glucose with hexokinase, this latter taking place inside the permeability barrier where the transport step is operative.

Indeed evidence is now accumulating that a specific transport step is involved in the uptake of sugars by yeast cells. Cramer and Woodward (1952) provided the first evidence in favour of such a step. They found that 2-desoxy-D-glucose (2DG) strongly inhibits the anaerobic fermentation of living yeast cells. The degree of inhibition is dependent upon the molar ratio of substrate to inhibitor but independent of the absolute concentration of substrate, of the number of yeast cells and of the pH of the medium. In marked contrast, the initial rate of fermentation of glucose by a cell-free extract (prepared by centrifugation from a 20 per cent. aqueous suspension of pressed yeast, fortified with ATP, diphosphopyridine nucleotide, inorganic phosphate and magnesium ions) is not inhibited by 2DG. The very slight inhibitory effect observed later may be explained by the consumption of ATP by the system in a non-reversible manner. The difference between the two systems was explained in terms of a step responsible for the transport of glucose into the yeast cell. The inhibitory action of 2DG was considered to be through it acting as a structural analogue to glucose.

Cramer and Woodward ruled out the possibility that the inhibition of fermentation in the living yeast cell could be due to depletion of ATP by 2DG. They showed that the inhibitory effect produced by adding 2DG to an actively fermenting system is exerted immediately and remains constant over a period of time. Exposure of yeast to 2DG before the addition of the substrate does not increase the amount of inhibition produced.

Burger, Hejmová and Kleinzeller (1959) studying the uptake of galactose and arabinose, both of which are not immediately metabolised by yeast cells, demonstrated the presence of a specific transport step for these sugars. They showed that the apparent intracellular concentration is never greater than in the external solution and is linearly related to the external sugar concentration. Phosphorylated derivatives could not be demonstrated within the cells.

A more detailed characterisation of the transport step came from studies on the effect of glucose on the intracellular concentration of galactose and arabinose. No free glucose can be demonstrated in yeast cells incubated with this sugar, either aerobically or anaerobically. However, in the presence of 1 mM iodoacetate, glucose can be demonstrated readily inside the cell. Addition of glucose to the medium greatly reduces the uptake of galactose. It was also found that on addition of glucose to a yeast suspension, which has been incubated previously for some

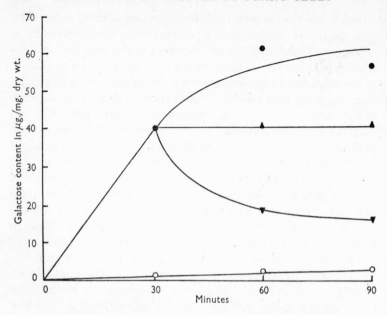

Fig. 19. The effect of glucose and iodoacetate on the absorption of galactose by yeast cells. Suspensions of cells were incubated anaerobically at 30° with 5% galactose. At 30 minutes, 1% (final concentration) glucose or glucose and 1 mM. iodoacetate was added. (●), control, 5% galactose; (▼), glucose added; (▲), glucose and iodoacetate added; (O), galactose and glucose added at zero time (Burger, Hejmová and Kleinzeller, 1959).

time in the presence of galactose and in which this sugar has penetrated into the cells, a rapid loss of galactose occurs. If however iodoacetate (1 mM final concentration) is added simultaneously with glucose, the intracellular concentration does not change (Fig. 19). The same type of response is observed with arabinose. The loss of sugar from the cells is decreased only in the presence of glucose plus iodoacetate. Glucose or iodoacetate alone are without effect. It is significant that no such inhibitory effect is observed with glucose when lower concentrations of iodoacetate (less than 0·5 mM) are used. Under these conditions, no glucose can be demonstrated inside the cells.

From these experiments, it appears that glucose only affects the loss of galactose from the cell when free glucose is present.

The above results may therefore be explained as follows. Glucose, when present in the medium but not intracellularly, inhibits galactose influx but not galactose efflux, in consequence of which there is a fall in the intracellular concentration of galactose. In the presence of iodoacetate, glucose is also present intracellularly and, under these conditions, inhibits both influx and efflux of galactose.

The evidence presented above is in favour of a passive mechanism for the transport of galactose and arabinose into the yeast cell. The lack of effect of iodoacetate, at a concentration which prevents completely the metabolism of glucose, and the lack of accumulation inside the cell against a concentration gradient suggest this. Burger *et al.* pointed out that the absorption of galactose and arabinose may be facilitated diffusion. They were not certain of the extent to which glucose is transported by such a process, for it remained possible that a portion of the glucose could be absorbed by a phosphorylating mechanism.

Cirillo (1961) has made further studies with results in accord with these observations. He has found that the following non-metabolisable sugars are transported into yeast cells by a stereo-specific carrier system: L-sorbose, L-galactose, D-xylose, D-arabinose, L-fucose, L-arabinose and D-ribose (in order of efficiency). The transport is independent of metabolic energy, and there is no accumulation in the cell against a concentration gradient. The transport shows what were described as Michaelis kinetics, and there is no accumulation of sugars in the cells against a concentration gradient. There is competitive inhibition between sugars for the transport system. The transport of sugars is inhibited by uranyl ions, and, furthermore, uranyl ions inhibit glucose utilisation and sorbose transport to the same degree. 'Counterflow' occurs between glucose and the non-metabolisable sugars—that is the exchange between a sugar in the external medium and a sugar inside the cell, such that the internal sugar moves out of the cell against a concentration gradient. All this data is consistent with the facilitated diffusion of monosaccharides into yeast cells.

The study of the permeability of micro-organisms to di-saccharides gained considerable impetus from those studies at the Institut Pasteur in Paris on the discrepancy between the β-galactosidase activity of cell-free preparations and intact cells of *Escherichia coli* (see Cohen and Monod (1957) for a review of this work).

It was found that there are cells which cannot metabolise β-galactosides, even though such cells contain the necessary enzymes for carrying out such metabolism. From a study of inducible and selected mutant strains and by using non-metabolisable thiogalactosides, it was shown that there is a transport step which is independent of the hydrolytic enzyme β-galactosidase, the presence of which is necessary to initiate the metabolism of the galactosides. The induction of the transport step shows all the characteristics of induced protein synthesis—induction is blocked by the absence of any required amino acid, by chloromycetin, an inhibitor of protein synthesis, and, significantly, the system is not formed in the presence of β-2-thienylalanine, a compound which does not inhibit protein synthesis in *E. coli* but which causes inactivation of the proteins into which it is incorporated. The transport step is therefore brought about through the functioning of a specific protein which was termed a 'permease'. The permease possesses many characteristics of an enzyme, in that uptake follows Michaelis kinetics, considerable stereospecificity is involved and the system shows considerable sensitivity to such enzyme inhibitors as p-chloromercuribenzoate. The uptake of galactosides appears to be an active process, the compounds being concentrated some 100 to 10,000 times. Absorption is inhibited by DNP.

Similar studies to those with *E. coli* led Robertson and Halvorson (1957) to postulate the presence of a permease for the absorption of maltose by yeast cells. Robertson and Halvorson found that maltose-grown cells, when shaken aerobically in the presence of glucose and in the absence of exogenous nitrogen, lose their maltozymase activity—this loss being known as de-adaptation. De-adaptation cannot be explained by a progressive inactivation of α-glucosidase. In fact, the cells become cryptic to maltose, that is the cells become unable to ferment maltose even though cell extracts still possess α-glucosidase activity. It is possible to explain this increase in crypticity by two alternative hypotheses. Either α-glucosidase is not a member of the maltozymase sequence, or α-glucosidase is a member of the maltozymase sequence but is not rate-limiting.

The evidence is in favour of the latter explanation. In genetic crosses, maltozymase activity has been so far always associated with α-glucosidase activity. There are no reported cases of fermentation of maltose by yeast cells in which α-glucosidase activity is not evident. Thus, there is a parallel induction of α-glucosidase activity in inducible strains, such that the malto-zymase activity can be quantitatively explained by the α-gluco-sidase activity. Furthermore, it is possible to separate permeation from cell metabolism by using α-methyl glucoside, which is not metabolised by the yeast cells. Experiments with this compound have shown that it is absorbed by the cells and is not lost from the cells during limited washing with cold water. Absorption follows Michaelis kinetics and is inhibited by 5×10^{-3} M DNP, 10^{-2} M sodium azide and 10^{-2} M sodium fluoride.

It is not clear from the data what actual mechanism is responsible for the absorption of α-glucosides. Active transport may be involved, for Cirillo (1961) has stated that the data of Robertson and Halvorson shows that α-methyl glucoside can be accumulated against a concentration gradient. However, he points out that, since accumulation is against a relatively small concentration gradient and since energy dependence for uptake has been determined by means of DNP sensitivity, at concentrations of DNP much higher than those necessary to uncouple phosphorylation, any conclusions concerning the active nature of the uptake process should be viewed with caution.

The likelihood of the occurrence of sugar transport in yeast through facilitated diffusion suggests that kinetic analysis of sugar uptake, from the aspect of interference between sugars for uptake, as described in Chapter 2, might define the system in an unambiguous manner.

It should be pointed out that Demis, Rothstein and Meier (1954) have shown that surface-located invertase accounts for essentially all the sucrose utilisation in yeast cells. The hexoses produced by hydrolysis are the actual molecular species involved in the uptake process.

Other cells

The uptake of glucose by *Scenedesmus quadricauda* has also been studied in detail (Taylor, 1960a and 1960b). A very interesting feature of the results is the reversal of the inhibition of glucose uptake in the presence of 4×10^{-5} M DNP and in the presence of 10^{-2} M phloridzin by the addition of ATP to the medium. ATP has no effect on the glucose uptake by fresh cells. On the other hand, cells grown on half the supply of phosphate absorb glucose at a significantly lower rate than normal cells. The rate of glucose uptake can be restored to the normal rate by the addition of ATP. Inorganic phosphate has no effect.

This evidence is strongly in favour of phosphorylative mechanisms being closely involved in the uptake of glucose by *Scenedesmus*. Taylor (1960b) suggests that the primary absorption mechanism is a hexokinase system situated on the outside of the plasma membrane. In view of what has already been said, a certain amount of caution is needed in accepting this conclusion. In any case, three facts suggest that hexokinase is not implicated in glucose uptake. First, the pH optimum for glucose uptake is much more acidic than for the majority of hexokinases extracted from various tissues and certainly more than that for yeast hexokinase. Second, the specific inhibitors of brain hexokinase, N-(p-nitrobenzoyl) glucosamine and N-(3 : 5-dinitrobenzoyl) glucosamine, while inhibiting glucose uptake, do so only mildly. Both compounds are powerful competitive inhibitors of the enzyme from brain, producing their effect at a concentration ten times lower than that used in the experiments with *Scenedesmus* (Maley and Lardy, 1955). Third, phloridzin, which has no effect on hexokinase (Rosenberg and Wilbrandt, 1952), inhibits glucose uptake, though in this case Taylor (1960b) suggests that a phosphatase responsible for the regeneration of ATP is the enzyme which is inhibited. Even if hexokinase is implicated in glucose uptake, it is possible that two hexokinases are involved, for there is a bi-phasic relationship between glucose uptake and the external glucose concentration.

There seems to be two alternative methods for the absorption of sucrose. Either the sucrose molecule is absorbed directly, or the molecule is inverted and the glucose and fructose moieties absorbed. Discs of *Peltigera polydactyla* and excised beech mycorrhizal roots appear to absorb sucrose in this manner (Harley and Smith, 1956; Harley and Jennings, 1958). Those factors which inhibit or diminish absorption bring about an increase of reducing sugars in the medium. On the other hand, inhibition of the inversion process brings about an associated decrease in the uptake of sucrose. The hexose absorption system shows a marked preference for glucose—there is a greater rate of glucose uptake than fructose uptake from mixed solutions. In agreement with the hypothesis that sucrose is not itself absorbed, the residual fructose remaining in solution, after absorption from sucrose or an equivalent solution of glucose and fructose, exceeds the residual glucose and is very similar in quantity in the two cases.

Leaf tissue of *Atropa belladona* appears to absorb sucrose without any intervening inversion process (Weatherley, 1953 and 1954; Pennell and Weatherley, 1958). There is certainly no connection between the rate of sucrose inversion and the rate of sucrose uptake. Sucrose absorption into the 'non-free space' is an aerobic process, and maltose competes for the same absorption sites.

There may be a third method by which sucrose is absorbed. Dormer and Street (1949) and Street and Lowe (1950) proposed that sucrose is absorbed by tomato roots through the mediation of a sucrose phosphyorylase, similar to that found by Doudoroff, Kaplan and Hassid (1943) in cells of *Pseudomonas saccharophila*, which brings about the reaction.

$$\text{Sucrose} + H_3PO_4 \rightleftharpoons \text{glucose-1-phosphate} + \text{fructose}$$

The evidence put forward for this mechanism comes from a variety of observations on the growth of excised tomato roots. Sucrose supports growth which is greatly superior to that with every other sugar tested. Neither glucose, nor fructose, nor an equimolar mixture of these two sugars are capable of supporting a growth in any way comparable to that obtained by using sucrose. Sucrose breakdown is quantitatively related to its utilisation. As well as this, phosphorus deficiency in the growth medium produces similar symptoms to those produced by carbohydrate deficiency. On the other hand, growth in the presence of sucrose shows marked indifference to phosphate concentration over the range 5·0-20·0 p.p.m., a concentration range over which an increased utilisation of sucrose should be observed if sucrose phosphorylase is involved in sucrose uptake. Furthermore other evidence put forward in support of the presence of phosphorylase—inhibition of sucrose absorption by phloridzin and the ratio of glucose to fructose found in the solution as a result of growth of the roots in a sucrose medium—can be explained equally in terms of inversion of sucrose and the subsequent uptake of the glucose and fructose moieties.

CHAPTER 14

COMMENT

It is clear from the previous chapters that there is now a plethora of experimental data about the movement of solutes between plant cells and their external media. The present chapter is concerned with a general discussion of the data. It does not seek to provide an all-embracing theory which explains the various experimental facts but intends to suggest significant features about these facts. Although much is known about the movements of dissolved substances between plant cells and their external media, many more facts are still required. For the present, the establishment of common relationships between various experimental facts is more important than the creation of any new theories. It is hoped that in the succeeding paragraphs certain relationships are indeed established and, where none exists, the suggestions which are put forward will provide some basis for future experimental work.

Plant cells and tissues can be considered as two phase systems with regard to dissolved substances in the external medium. The one phase, the outer region of unicells, and the free space of plant tissues, is, relatively speaking, freely accessible to the external medium. On the other hand, the association of solutes with the other phase, the inner space of unicells and the non-free space of tissues, is governed by the presence of various permeability barriers.

The free space of plant cells and tissues is most probably located in the cell wall, though for tissues there is the additional component, the intercellular spaces. The evidence in favour of this location of the free space has been drawn from studies on isolated cell walls. On the other hand, it is apparent that, if the cytoplasm is associated with the free space, only a small proportion of this cellular entity can be involved. The probable peripheral location of a major permeability barrier for potassium, sodium and bivalent cations in large algal cells must mean that a large portion of the cytoplasm is not freely

M

accessible to electrolytes. The exact contribution of the purely structural units of the cell wall to the fixed anionic groups within the free space is not clear but it must be considerable. The cytoplasm probably makes some small contribution to the number of non-mobile anions, as seems to be the case for the polyphosphate groups at the surface of the yeast cell which have been shown to bind strongly bivalent ions.

It is apparent, from the data presented in the previous chapters, that, where the entry of a solute into the non-free space is associated with the metabolism of the cell, few generalities can be made. Not only does it appear that different compounds are absorbed by different mechanisms, but, for the same compound, more than one mechanism may be involved in bringing about the entry of the compound into the cell. Two distinct pathways for glucose entry can be identified in yeast cells, differing in their sensitivity to uranium and associated with different metabolic pathways inside the cell. Likewise, two absorption mechanisms, which are metabolically controlled, exist in yeast for the uptake of magnesium and manganese. The same may apply for other solutes. On the other hand, it does not seem that there is a separate absorption mechanism for each solute which is absorbed. The knowledge that we have clearly indicates that most absorption mechanisms have a fairly wide specificity. Potassium, rubidium and sodium are absorbed by the same mechanism in a variety of cells, as are calcium and strontium, magnesium and manganese, sulphate and selenate and glucose, fructose and mannose.

The influence of metabolism on the aborption of any solute can be demonstrated simply through the use of inhibitors and anaerobic conditions. However, the identification of that point at which metabolism exerts its effect can prove to be much more difficult. In the introductory chapter, it was explained that the concept of active transport has been invoked to explain the accumulation within cells of non-electrolytes against an activity of ions against an electrochemical activity gradient. There is no reason to suppose that active transport mechanisms are not present, even where the solute is not moving against an activity gradient. This could occur in those cells which are relatively impermeable, under conditions in which metabolism is reduced to a minimum, to the solute in question. For the active transport mechanism can not only be considered as a mechanism responsible for the accumulation of the solute within the cell but also as the force moving the solute across a permeability barrier. It is clear that the inability to observe an activity gradient acting against solute movement does not necessarily preclude that the solute is being transported into the cell. Such may be the case when the solute is metabolised within the cell, since the rate of metabolism of the solute, once it has entered the cell, may be such that movement into the cell is never against an activity gradient.

Metabolism may also effect solute absorption as a result of chemical combination of the solute with a cellular constituent. However, studies on phosphate entry into a variety of cells emphasise the necessity of not presupposing that compounds closely associated with intermediary metabolism must be absorbed into the cell, either as a result of combination with a metabolite or as a result of chemical change.

The tendency of any ionic system to move towards electro-neutrality complicates any kinetic analysis and makes it technically difficult to separate the various factors governing electrolyte movements between the cell and the external medium. It is only with some difficulty that it can be determined which ion of any pair is moved by some driving force and which accompanies the other in order to satisfy electro-neutrality. There may be an added complication in that the movement of one ion into the cell is specifically connected with the movement of another ion out of the cell, as is the case for certain animal tissues where that potassium movement into the cell is specifically coupled with sodium movement out of the cell. While the exact location of the driving force may be difficult to discern, the rate of movement of the slowest member of any pair may govern the rate of movement of the other ion. Hurd (1958 and 1959) showed that this is the case for storage tissues where the rate of potassium uptake is governed by the rate of the accompanying anion. Those tissues which are more permeable to bicarbonate than chloride ions show a greater absorption of potassium in the presence of the former than in the presence of the latter ions.

Studies on large algal cells promise the most fruitful approach to the problem of the active transport of electrolytes. With these cells it is possible to distinguish the various ion fluxes and measure simultaneously the electro-chemical potential changes. The results described in Chapter 3 show the advantage of such studies, and such studies emphasise that active transport mechanisms moving ions *out* of the cell may be a factor determining the internal ionic environment of the cell. In fact, the movements of a number of substances between plant cells and the external medium cannot be considered solely in terms of net fluxes. The data obtained for potassium movements in various cells show that the net movement of the ion must be considered in terms of inward and outward fluxes, each differing in their response to various factors and in their affinity for the ion itself. Glutamic acid accumulation in bacteria appears to be the net result of inward and outward fluxes differing in their respective properties. Even so, some cells have been shown to be permeable to certain ions in one direction only. Manganous ions absorbed by yeast cells and phosphate ions absorbed by the same cells and by beech mycorrhizal roots show no capacity to exchange with ions in the external medium.

The specific mechanisms involved in the movement of solutes between the cell and the external medium may be located in a variety of locations throughout the cell. Rothstein (1956) has stressed the location of various permeability barriers at different depths in the yeast cell. The studies with large algal cells suggest that the active transport mechanism for chloride uptake is located at the tonoplast, whilst the active transport mechanism moving sodium out of the cell is located near the outer surface, probably at the plasmalemma.

The coupling between metabolism and the mechanisms responsible for active transport is suggested to be phosphorylative. Sulphydryl groups appear to be important in maintaining the permeability properties of yeast, though it is not clear how far such groups are concerned, if at all, with the active transport of electrolytes. The importance of these groups may be widespread. Tanada (1956) showed that the uptake of rubidium by mung bean roots is affected by sulphydryl inhibitors, such as phenyl mercuric nitrate. Under certain conditions, rubidum uptake is markedly reduced. Considering the data obtained with yeast at the molecular level, Falcone and Nickerson (1956) (see also Nickerson and Falcone, 1956) have isolated a protein containing sulphydryl groups from the yeast cell wall, which may be identical with the mercury binding sites observed by Passow and Rothstein (1960).

It is not clear whether the coupling between phosphorylation and active transport mechanisms is direct or indirect. The isolation from nerve cells and erythrocytes of adenosinetriphosphatases having a number of the necessary characteristics of the respective transport systems responsible for potassium and sodium movements in these cells has provided striking evidence that the linkage can be direct. It is possible that magnesium transport into yeast cells is directly mediated by a similar enzyme, in view of the importance of magnesium ions in phosphorylation reactions and the necessity for phosphate absorption to take place previous to magnesium absorption. Similarly, a hexokinase or hexokinase-like enzyme might be responsible for sugar transport into some plant cells. On the other hand, for the transport of other substances one or more enzymes may be interposed between the phosphorylating system and the transport mechanism. In these cases, the influence of phosphorylation reactions will probably be unspecific.

This focuses attention on those problems which must be associated with the search for 'carriers' or molecules responsible for the movement of substances from the external medium into a plant cell. There are considerable difficulties involved in identifying a carrier with any molecule extracted from a cell, for it is probable that the properties and consequently the functioning of any carrier will depend on associated molecules and structural orientation. An example of this type of interaction is to be found in the studies upon those enzymes comprising the respiratory chain, in particular the succinic dehydrogenase-cytochrome system. This system can be obtained associated with particles derived from physically disintegrated mitochondria. When succinic dehydrogenase is isolated in soluble form, it is very unstable and does not react with cytochrome c. However, when the soluble form is re-incorporated within the particulate preparation, it re-acquires its stability and its ability to react with cytochrome c (Keilin, 1959). Any success that occurs in the search for a carrier may depend upon the availability of a specific inhibitor for the transport process.

In Chapter 5, the use of cardiac glycosides for such a purpose was described. These compounds inhibit in a comparable manner both the potassium and sodium movements in nerve cells and erythrocytes and the activity of the adenosine triphosphatases extracted from the peripheral membranes of these cells. This evidence together with other data points in an unambiguous manner to the functioning of these enzymes in the transport process. However, the identification of a major component of the carrier does no more than give a sketch of the function of the enzyme. The stoichiometry of the system remains obscure, for the means whereby the removal of the terminal phosphate group of an ATP molecule can bring about the movement of two ions in opposite direction are not immediately apparent.

The ease with which it is possible to study the effect of external factors on absorption processes is in marked contrast to the ignorance concerning the influence of intracellular factors on the absorption of any solute from the external medium. It is probable that the intracellular concentration of the solute will influence the rate of absorption from the external medium. It has long been appreciated that the total ion content of a tissue has an important influence on the rate of ion absorption and this fact has been epitomised by the tradition of using 'low salt' plants to induce a high rate of salt uptake. Sutcliffe (1952) showed that the rate of uptake of potassium by red beet discs is related to their potassium content. However, the level of potassium finally attained is independent of the initial level of potassium. There is no evidence to suggest the factors which govern the final level of potassium within the tissue, but total ion content must be an important factor. The final level of potassium is certainly not governed in an absolute manner. Hurd (1959) showed that beet discs kept in potassium chloride solutions and potassium bicarbonate solutions of the same concentrations, for periods of time sufficiently long to ensure that no further absorption was possible, have widely differing final potassium concentrations—those from potassium bicarbonate solutions having a much higher potassium content. The difference in accompanying anion had no effect on the system absorbing potassium, since, after allowing the discs to complete the maximum absorption of potassium in one solution, bathing the discs in the alternate solution caused no further decrease or increase of the potassium content. Earlier, Hurd (1958) had shown that the uptake of potassium bicarbonate is accompanied by an increase in the malic acid content of beet tissue. An increase in the anion content in this manner might account for the greater level of potassium achieved with cells which absorb potassium bicarbonate.

At the present time there are few points of comparison between studies on solute movements between plant cells and the external medium and comparable studies with animal cells. MacRobbie and Dainty (1958) have compared ion fluxes in *Nitellopsis* with ion fluxes in squid nerves and in muscle. Flux data are an important point of comparison, though these comparisons may be only satisfactory when more is known about the mechanisms involved in electrolyte movements in both types of tissue. Solute movements in animal tissues are complicated by the effects of hormones. Insulin has no effect on the glucose uptake by yeast (A. Rothstein, personal communication) or by *Peltigera polydactyla* (D. C. Smith, personal communication). Conway and Hingerty (1953) found that deoxycorticosterone and cortisone showed significant but not very marked effects on the uptake of potassium and sodium by fermenting yeast. Pickles and Sutcliffe (1955) showed that serotonin (5-hydroxytryptamine) increased the loss of pigment from red beet and strongly inhibited the sodium uptake by the same issue. Studies with compounds which affect the electrolyte balance of animal cells might in certain circumstances provide a valuable tool for studying solute movements in plant cells.

Up to this point, all that has been said has been from the traditional standpoint. The plant cell has been considered as a system osmotically isolated from its extracellular environment, and the discussion of the data has centred upon the ways and means whereby ions or molecules can pass through the osmotic boundaries of the cell, possibly being accumulated against a concentration gradient. This is of course a simplification, for the various aspects of the discussion throughout this book reflect the very much more sophisticated outlook of all investigators concerned with the relationship of solutes and plant cells. Nevertheless, it would not be false historiography to suggest that even today much physiological thinking has its origins in the statement of Claude Bernard, 'La fixité du milieu intérier est la condition de vie libre.' While, admittedly, this originally applied to organisms, the influence of such thoughts as these upon cell physiology should not be ignored. It is for this reason that this last comment contains the suggestion that the most profitable approach to many of the manifold problems, brought to light by the study of the relationships between solutes and plant cells, may be through a questioning of the adequacy of the present basic tenets and assumptions. A reappraisal of the fundamental questions which the experimentalist must ask himself may be more fruitful than a consideration of new hypotheses based upon questions no longer relevant.

The value of radical rethinking of the fundamental assumptions can best be demonstrated by reference to some stimulating suggestions made by Mitchell (1961) to explain the coupling of phosphorylation to electron and hydrogen transfer in mitochondria. Mitchell has pointed out that there are a number of facts about the functioning of these subcellular particles in the production of ATP from ADP and inorganic phosphate, as the result of hydrogen transfer from such substrates as succinic acid through the cytochrome system to molecular oxygen, which are difficult to reconcile in terms of orthodox chemical hypotheses concerning the nature of the mechanism involved. Among the facts are these:

(a) Hypothetical 'high energy' intermediates, which have to be postulated on the basis of orthodox chemical hypotheses, are elusive to identification.

(b) It is not clear why phosphorylation should be closely associated with membranous structures. There is very strong evidence from combined electron microscopical and biochemical studies that the 'double' membrane of the mitochondrion is absolutely necessary for phosphorylation at the electron transfer level.

(c) Uncoupling of phosphorylation from electron transfer can be caused at all three hypothetical oxido-reduction sites in the mitochondrion by agents that do not share identifiable specific chemical characteristics.

(d) Unexplained swelling and shrinkage phenomena accompany the activity of the phosphorylation mechanism.

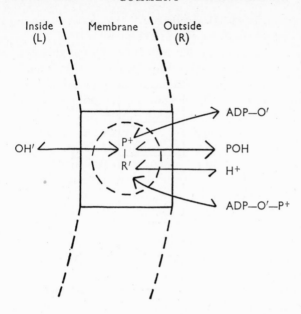

FIG. 20. A schematic representation of an anisotopic reversible 'ATPase' system located in an ion-impermeable membrane between aqueous phases L and R (Mitchell, 1961).

Mitchell has proposed that the spatial arrangements of various elements of the phosphorylating system are a key factor in the functioning of the system. He has proposed that a basic feature of the system is a membrane-located reversible adenosine triphosphatase (ATPase) system, which is shown diagrammatically in Fig. 20. The enzyme is assumed to be anisotropic, in that the active centre (indicated by the dotted circle) is accessible to hydroxyl ions, but not to hydrogen ions, from the left and to hydrogen ions, but not hydroxyl ions, from the right. The active centre like that of phosphokinases in general is assumed to be inaccessible to water as water.

The hypothesis developed by Mitchell depends thermodynamically on the fact that in such a system the electrochemical activity of the water at the active centre $[H_2O]_C$, which determines the equilibrium ATP/ADP, would be governed not by the product $[H^+][OH']$ in the combined

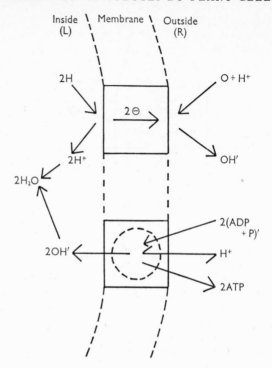

FIG. 21. A schematic representation of an electron transport system (above) and a reversible 'ATPase' system (below) chemi-osmotically coupled in a charge-impermeable membrane between aqueous phases *L* and *R* (Mitchell, 1961).

aqueous phases but by the product $[H^+]_R[OH']_L$, where the brackets stand for electrochemical activity and R and L stand for right- and left-hand phases respectively. Consequently, from the mass action equilibrium

$$\frac{[ATP]}{[ADP]} = \frac{[P]}{K[H_2O]_C},$$

where $K =$ the equilibrium constant.

Furthermore, the electrochemical activity of water at the active centre is given by

$$[H_2O]_C = [H_2O]aq \cdot \frac{[H^+]_R}{[H^+]_L}.$$

Mitchell has shown that it is possible to have physiologically feasible hydrogen ion concentrations on either side of the membrane such that the equilibrium is in favour of ATP formation.

The coupling of electron transfer to phosphorylation also depends upon an anisotropic electron and hydrogen transfer system. Its relation to the anisotropic ATPase is shown in Fig. 21. The arrangement is such that the active centre is 'dehydrated' with subsequent synthesis of ATP.

The above is only a brief sketch of what Mitchell has suggested. The detailed suggestions provide an answer to the problems outlined above. For instance, the need for the 'high energy' intermediates is removed. An explanation is also offered for the variety of causes bringing about the uncoupling of phosphorylation from electron transfer, for coupling would be expected to vary with the extent of leakiness or strain on the membrane which, in turn, is determined by the osmotic or electrical stress. Lipide-soluble agents such as DNP, salicylate, azide and ammonia will catalyse the equilibration of hydrogen ions and hydroxyl ions across the membrane. A charge-impermeable membrane would be the requirement of efficient coupling. From the reverse point of view, the coupling of phos-phorylation to electron and hydrogen transfer will obviously cause considerable electrical and osmotic stress to the membrane system, consequently complex swelling and shrinkage pheno-mena would be expected.

Mitchell (1959) has termed such metabolic phenomena as described above a *chemi-osmotic process*, because the driving force on a given chemical reaction can be due to the spatially directed channelling of the diffusion of a chemical component or group along a pathway specified in space by the physical organisation of the system. The underlying thesis put forward by Mitchell is that, if processes of metabolism and transport represent steps in a sequence, not only can metabolism be the cause of transport but transport can also be the cause of metabolism.

It may be that certain of the data presented in this book concern chemi-osmotic processes. Those considering transport phenomena in plant cells would probably not be interested initially in the membrane systems of the mitochondria or, for that matter, those of chloroplasts (where phosphorylation is driven by the energy of absorbed photons). A more likely candidate for consideration would be the plasmalemma. In view of the fact that this region of the cell is the site of wall synthesis, it may be that considerations of a chemi-osmotic nature might provide an answer to some of the problems raised by the presence of marked organisation amongst the fibriller elements in the wall, not least of which is the effect of indole-acetic acid on wall extensibility.

REFERENCES

ARENZ, B., 1941: Beitrag zur physiologischen Auswirkung von Ammoniak und Nitratstickstoff. *Biochem. Z.* **308**, 196-212.

ARISZ, W. H., 1945: Contribution to a theory on the absorption of salts by the plant and their transport in parenchymatous tissue. *Proc. Acad. Sci. Amst.* **48**, 420-446.

    1956: Significance of the symplasm theory for transport across the root. *Protoplasma*, **46**, 5-62.

    1958: Influence of inhibitors on the uptake and the transport of chloride ions in the leaves of *Vallisneria spiralis*. *Acta Bot. Neerl.* **7**, 1-32.

ARMSTRONG, W. McD., 1957: Surface-active agents and cellular metabolism. I. Effect of cationic detergents on the production of acid and carbon dioxide by baker's yeast. *Arch. Biochem.* **71**, 137-147.

ARNON, D. I., 1937: Ammonium and nitrate nitrogen of barley at different seasons in relation to hydrogen ion concentration, manganese, copper and oxygen supply. *Soil Sci.* **44**, 91-113.

ARNON, D. I., W. E. FRATZKE and C. M. JOHNSTON, 1942: Hydrogen ion concentration in relation to absorption of inorganic nutrients by higher plants. *Plant Physiol.* **17**, 515-524.

ASPREY, G. F., 1937: Some observations on the absorption and exosmosis of electrolytes by storage organs with particular reference to potato and artichoke tubers. *Protoplasma*, **27**, 153-168.

BECKING, J. H., 1956: The mechanism of ammonium ion uptake by maize roots. *Acta Bot. Neerl.* **5**, 1-79.

BENNET, M. C. and E. RIDEAL, 1954: Membrane behaviour in *Nitella*. *Proc. roy. Soc. B*, **142**, 483-496.

BENNET-CLARK, T. A. and D. BEXON, 1943: Water relations of plant cells. III. The respiration of plasmolysed tissues. *New Phytol.* **42**, 65-92.

BERGER, L., M. W. STEIN, S. P. COLOWICK and C. F. CORI, 1946: Isolation of hexokinase from baker's yeast. *J. gen. Physiol.* **29**, 379-391.

BERRY, W. E. and F. C. STEWARD, 1934: The absorption and accumulation of solutes by living plant cells. VI. The absorption of potassium bromide from dilute solution by tissue from various plant storage organs. *Ann. Bot.* **48**, 395-410.

BHIDE, S. V. and J. BRACHET, 1960: Study on the uptake of ribonuclease by onion root-tip cells. *Exp. Cell Res.* **21**, 303-315.

BIRT, L. M. and F. J. R. HURD, 1956: The uptake of amino acids by carrot slices. *Biochem. J.* **64**, 305-311.

    1958a: The uptake and metabolism of amino acids by slices of carrot. *Biochem. J.* **70**, 277-286.

    1958b: Kinetic aspects of the uptake of amino acids by carrot tissue. *Biochem. J.* **70**, 286-292.

BLINKS, L. R., 1930: The direct current resistance of *Nitella*. *J. gen. Physiol.* **13**, 495-508.

BLINKS, L.R., 1932: Protoplasmic potentials in *Halicystis*. II. The effects of potassium on two species with different saps. *J. gen. Physiol.* **16**, 147-156.

— 1935: Protoplasmic potentials in *Halicystis*. IV. Vacuolar perfusion with artificial sap and sea water. *J. gen. Physiol.* **81**, 409-420.

— 1940: The relations of bioelectrical phenomena to ionic permeability and metabolism in large plant cells. *Cold Spring Harbor Symp.* **8**, 204-215.

BLOUNT, R. W. and B. H. LEVEDAHL, 1960: Active sodium and chloride transport in the single celled marine alga *Halicystis ovalis*. *Acta physiol. scand.* **49**, 1-9.

BONNER, J., 1946: The role of organic matter, especially manure, in the nutrition of rice. *Bot. Gaz.* **108**, 267-279.

BOWYER, F., 1957: The kinetics of the penetration of non-electrolytes into the mammalian erythrocyte. *Intern. Rev. Cytol.* **6**, 469-511.

BRIGGS, G. E., 1957a: Ion permeability of the plasmalemma of the plant cell. *Nature, Lond.* **180**, 1142-1143.

— 1957b: Some aspects of free space in plant tissues. *New Phytol.* **56**, 305-324.

— 1957c: Estimations of the flux of ions into and out of the vacuole of a plant cell. *J. exp. Bot.* **8**, 319-322.

BRIGGS, G. E., A. B. HOPE and M. G. PITMAN, 1958a: Exchangeable ions in beet disks at low temperature. *J. exp. Bot.* **9**, 128-141.

— 1958b: Measurement of ionic fluxes in red beet tissue using radio-isotopes. *Radioisotopes in Scientific Research* (ed. R. C. Extermann). London, Pergammon Press, **4**, 391-400.

BRIGGS, G. E. and R. N. ROBERTSON, 1948: Diffusion and absorption in disks of plant tissue. *New Phytol.* **47**, 265-283.

— 1957: Apparent free space. *Annu. Rev. Pl. Physiol.* **8**, 11-30.

BROOKS, S. C., 1940: The intake of radioactive isotopes by living cells. *Cold Spring Harbour Symp.* **8**, 171-177.

BROYER, T. C., 1950: Further observations on the absorption and trans-location of inorganic solutions using radioactive isotopes with plants. *Plant Physiol.* **25**, 367-376.

BURGER, M., E. E. BACON and J. S. D. BACON, 1958: Liberation of invertase from disintegrated yeast cells. *Nature, Lond.* **182**, 1508.

— 1961: Form and location of invertase in the yeast cell. *Biochem. J.* **78**, 504-511.

BURGER, M., L. HEJMOVÁ and A. KLEINZELLER, 1959: Transport of some mono- and di-saccharides into yeast cells. *Biochem. J.* **71**, 233-242.

BUTLER, G. W., 1953a: Ion uptake by young wheat plants. II. The 'apparent free space' of wheat roots. *Physiol. Plant.* **6**, 617-635.

— 1953b: Ion uptake by young wheat plants. III. Phosphate absorption by excised roots. *Physiol. Plant.* **6**, 637-631.

CALDWELL, P. C. and R. D. KEYNES, 1957: The ultilisation of phosphate bond energy for sodium extrusion from giant axons. *J. Physiol.* **137**, 12.

CALO, N., J. MARKS and J. E. VARNER, 1957: Respiratory metabolism of aerated potato discs. *Nature, Lond.* **180**, 1142.

CHANCE, B. and G. R. WILLIAMS, 1956: The respiratory chain and oxidative phosphorylation. *Advanc. Enzymol.* **17**, 65-134.

CIRILLO, V. P., 1961: Sugar transport in microorganisms. *Annu. Rev. Microbiol.* **15**, 197-218.

COHEN, G. N. and J. MONOD, 1957: Bacterial permeases. *Bact. Rev.* **21**, 169-194.

COLE, K. S. and J. H. CURTIS, 1938: Electric impedance of *Nitella* during activity. *J. gen. Physiol.* **22**, 37-64.

COLLANDER, R., 1942: Die Elektrolyt-Permeabilität und Salz-Akkumulation pflanzlichen Zellen. *Tabul. biol.* (*Hague*), **19**, 313-333.

CONWAY, E. J. and M. E. BEARY, 1958: Active transport of magnesium across the yeast cell membrane. *Biochem. J.* **69**, 275-280.

CONWAY, E. J. and T. G. BRADY, 1950: Biological production of acid and alkali. 1. Quantitative relations of succinic and carbonic acids to the potassium and hydrogen-exchange in fermenting yeast. *Biochem. J.* **47**, 360-369.

CONWAY, E. J. and M. DOWNEY, 1950: An outer metabolic region of the yeast cell. *Biochem. J.* **47**, 347-355.

CONWAY, E. J. and P. F. DUGGAN, 1956: A general cation carrier in yeast cell wall—General carrier and its amount/kgm. yeast. *Nature, Lond.* **136**, 1043.

1958: A cation carrier in the yeast cell wall. *Biochem. J.* **69**, 265-274.

CONWAY, E. J. and D. HINGERTY, 1953: The effects of cortisone, deoxycorticosterone and other steroids on the active transport of sodium and potassium in yeast. *Biochem. J.* **55**, 455-458.

CONWAY, E. J. and R. P. KERNAN, 1955: The effect of redox dyes on the active transport of hydrogen, potassium and sodium ions across the yeast cell membrane. *Biochem. J.* **61**, 32-36.

CONWAY, E. J. and P. T. MOORE, 1954: A sodium-rich yeast and its properties. *Biochem. J.* **57**, 523-528.

CONWAY, E. J. and E. O'MALLEY, 1946: The nature of cation exchanges during yeast fermentation with formation of 0·02 normal H ion. *Biochem. J.* **40**, 59-67.

CONWAY, E. J., H. RYAN and E. CARTON, 1954: Active transport of sodium ions from the yeast cell. *Biochem. J.* **58**, 158-167.

CRAMER, F. B. and G. E. WOODWARD, 1952: 2-desoxy-D-glucose as an antagonist of glucose in yeast fermentation. *J. Franklin Inst.* **253**, 354-360.

CRAMER, M. and J. MYERS, 1949: Nitrate reductions and assimilation in *Chlorella. J. gen. Physiol.* **32**, 93-102.

DAINTY, J., 1960: Electrical analogues in biology. *Symp. Soc. exp. Biol.* **14**, 140-151.

DAINTY, J. and A. B. HOPE, 1959: Ionic relations of cells of *Chara australis.* *I.* Ion exchange in the cell wall. *Aust. J. Biol. Sci.* **12**, 395-411.

DANGEARD, P., 1928a: Sur l'iodovolatilisation et ses caractères chez les algues septantrionales. *C. R. Acad. Sci., Paris*, **187**, 899-901.

1928b: Action favorisante de l'iodure de potassium sur l'iodovolatilisation. *C. R. Acad. Sci., Paris*, **187**, 1156-1158.

DANGEARD, P., 1930: Sur l'obtention aux depens des Laminaires d'un complexe iodé labile. *C. R. Acad. Sci., Paris*, **191**, 337-339.

DANIELLI, J. F., 1943: In *The permeability of natural membranes* (By H. Davson and J. F. Danielli). Cambridge, Univ. Press, 361 pp.

— 1952: Structural factors in cell permeability and secretion. *Symp. Soc. exp. Biol.* **6**, 1-15.

DAVIS, R., J. P. FOLKES, E. F. GALE and L. C. BIGGAR, 1953: The assimilation of amino acids by micro-organisms. 16. Changes in sodium and potassium accompanying the accumulation of glutamic acid or lysine by bacteria and yeast. *Biochem. J.* **54**, 430-437.

DEMIS, D. J., A. ROTHSTEIN and R. MEIER, 1954: The relationship of the cell surface to metabolism. X. The location and function of invertase in the yeast cell. *Arch. Biochem.* **48**, 55-62.

DIAMOND, J. M. and A. K. SOLOMON, 1959: Intracellular potassium compartments in *Nitella axillaris*. *J. gen. Physiol.* **42**, 1105-1121.

DORMER, K. J. and H. E. STREET, 1949: The carbohydrate nutrition of tomato roots. *Ann. Bot. N.S.* **13**, 199-217.

DOUDOROFF, M., N. KAPLAN and W. Z. HASSID, 1943: Phosphorolysis and synthesis of sucrose with a bacterial preparation. *J. Biol. Chem.* **148**, 67-75.

DUNHAM, E. T. and I. M. GLYNN, 1961: Adenosine triphosphatase activity and the active movements of alkali metal ions. *J. Physiol.* **156**, 274-293.

EL-SHISHINY, E. D. H., 1955: Absorption and assimilation of inorganic nitrogen from different sources by storage root tissue. *J. exp. Bot.* **6**, 6-16.

EL-SHISHINY, E. D. H. and M. A. NOSSIER, 1957a: The relation of optical form to the utilization of amino acids. I. Utilization of stereoisomeric forms of glutamic acid by carrot root discs. *Plant Physiol.* **32**, 360-364.

— 1957b: The relation of optical form to the utilization of amino acids. II. Utilization of stereoisomeric varieties of aspartic acid and aspargine by carrot root discs. *Plant Physiol.* **32**, 639-643.

EPPLEY, R. W., 1958a: Sodium exclusion and potassium retention by the red marine alga, *Porphyra perforata*. *J. gen. Physiol.* **41**, 901-911.

— 1958b: Potassium-dependent sodium extrusion by cells of *Porphyra perforata*, a red marine alga. *J. gen. Physiol.* **42**, 281-288.

— 1959: Potassium accumulation and sodium efflux by *Porphyra perforata* tissues in lithium and magnesium sea water. *J. gen. Physiol.* **43**, 29-38.

EPPLEY, R. W. and C. C. CYRUS, 1960: Cation regulation and survival of the red alga, *Porphyra perforata*, in diluted and concentrated sea water. *Biol. Bull., Wood's Hole*, **118**, 55-65.

EPSTEIN, E., 1953: Mechanism of ion absorption by roots. *Nature, Lond.* **171**, 83-84.

— 1955: Passive permeation and active transport of ions in plant roots. *Plant Physiol.* **30**, 529-535.

— 1960: Calcium-lithium competition in absorption by plant roots. *Nature, Lond.* **185**, 705-706.

EPSTEIN, E., 1961: The essential role of calcium in selective cation transport by plant cells. *Plant Physiol.* **36**, 437-444.

EPSTEIN, E. and C. E. HAGEN, 1952: A kinetic study of the absorption of alkali cations by barley roots. *Plant Physiol.* **27**, 457-474.

EPSTEIN, E. and J. E. LEGGETT, 1954: The absorption of alkaline earth cations by barley roots: kinetics and mechanism. *Amer. J. Bot.* **41**, 783-792.

FALCONE, G. and W. J. NICKERSON, 1956: Cell-wall mannan—protein of baker's yeast. *Science*, **124**, 272-273.

FAWZY, H., R. OVERSTREET and L. JACOBSON, 1954: The influence of hydrogen ion concentration on cation absorption by barley roots. *Plant Physiol.* **29**, 234-237.

FINDLAY, G. P., 1959: Studies of action potentials in the vacuole and cytoplasm of *Nitella*. *Aust. J. Biol. Sci.* **12**, 412-426.

FOULKES, E. C., 1956: Cation transport in yeast. *J. gen. Physiol.* **39**, 687-704.

FREI, E. and R. D. PRESTON, 1961: Cell wall organization and wall growth in the filamentous green algae *Cladophora* and *Chaetomorpha*. I. The basic structure and its formation. *Proc. roy. Soc. B*, **154**, 70-94.

FRIIS, J. and P. OTTOLENGHI, 1959a: Localisation of invertase in a strain of yeast. *C. R. Lab. Carlsberg. Ser. Physiol.* **31**, 259-271.

1959b: Localisation of melibiase in a strain of yeast. *C. R. Lab. Carlsberg. Ser. Physiol.* **31**, 272-281.

GAFFEY, C. T. and L. J. MULLINS, 1958: Ion fluxes during the active potential in *Chara*. *J. Physiol.* **144**, 505-524.

GALE, E. F., 1945: Studies in bacterial amino acid decarboxylases. 5. The use of specific decarboxylase preparations in the estimation of amino acids and in protein analysis. *Biochem. J.* **39**, 46-52.

1947: The assimilation of amino acids by bacteria. 1. The passage of certain amino acids across the cell wall and their concentration in the internal environment of *Streptococcus faecalis*. *J. gen. Microbiol.* **1**, 53-76.

1951: The assimilation of amino acids by bacteria. 10. The action of inhibitors on the accumulation of free glutamic acid in *Staphylococcus aureus* and *Streptococcus faecalis*. *Biochem. J.* **48**, 286-290.

GALE, E. F. and M. B. VAN HALTEREN, 1951: The assimilation of amino acids by bacteria. 13. The effect of certain amino acids on the accumulation of free glutamic acid by *Staphylococcus aureus*: extracellular peptide formation. *Biochem. J.* **50**, 34-43.

GALE, E. F. and K. McQUILLEN, 1957: Nitrogen metabolism: with special reference to the synthesis of proteins and nucleic acids. *Annu. Rev. Microbiol.* **11**, 283-316.

GÁRDOS, G., 1954: Akkumulation der Kaliumionen durch menschiliche Blutkorperchen. *Acta. Physiol. Hung.* **6**, 191-199.

GLYNN, I. M., 1956: Sodium and potassium movements in human red cells. *J. Physiol.* **134**, 278-310.

1957: The action of cardiac glycosides on sodium and potassium movements in human red cells. *J. Physiol.* **136**, 148-173.

N

GLYNN, I. M., 1957: The ionic permeability of the red cell membrane. *Progr. Biophys.* **8**, 241-308.

1959: Sodium and potassium movements in nerve, muscle and red cells. *Intern. Rev. Cytol.* **8**, 449-480.

GOLD, G. L. and A. K. SOLOMON, 1955: The transport of sodium into human erythrocytes *in vivo*. *J. gen. Physiol.* **38**, 389-404.

GOODMAN, J. and A. ROTHSTEIN, 1957: The active transport of phosphate into the yeast cell. *J. gen. Physiol.* **40**, 915-923.

HACKETT, D. P., D. W. HASS, S. K. GRIFFITHS and D. J. NIEDERPRUEM, 1960: Studies on development of cyanide-resistant respiration in potato tuber slices. *Plant Physiol.* **35**, 8-19.

HAGEN, C. E. and H. T. HOPKINS, 1955: Ionic species in orthophosphate absorption by barley roots. *Plant Physiol.* **30**, 193-199.

HARLEY, J. L. and J. K. BRIERLEY, 1954: The uptake of phosphate by excised mycorrhizal roots of the beech. VI. Active transport of phosphate from the fungal sheath into the host tissue. *New Phytol.* **53**, 240-252.

1955: The uptake of phosphate by excised mycorrhizal roots of the beech. VII. Active transport of ^{32}P from fungus to host during uptake of phosphate from solution. *New Phytol.* **54**, 296-301.

HARLEY, J. L. and D. H. JENNINGS, 1958: The effects of sugars on the respiratory response of beech mycorrhizas to salts. *Proc. roy. Soc. B.* **148**, 403-418.

HARLEY, J. L. and C. C. McCREADY, 1950: The uptake of phosphate by excised mycorrhizal roots of the beech. *New Phytol.* **49**, 388-397.

HARLEY, J. L., C. C. McCREADY and J. K. BRIERLEY, 1953: The uptake of phosphate by excised mycorrhizal roots of the beech. IV. The effect of oxygen concentration upon host and fungus. *New. Phytol.* **52**, 124-132.

1958: The uptake of phosphate by excised mycorrhizal roots of the beech. VIII. Translocation of phosphorus in mycorrhizal roots. *New Phytol.* **57**, 353-362.

HARLEY, J. L., C. C. McCREADY, J. K. BRIERLEY and D. H. JENNINGS, 1956: The salt respiration of excised beech mycorrhizas. II. The relationship between oxygen consumption and phosphate absorption. *New Phytol.* **55**, 1-28.

HARLEY, J. L., C. C. McCREADY and J. A. GEDDES, 1954: The salt respiration of excised beech mycorrhizas. I. The development of the respiratory response to salts. *New Phytol.* **53**, 429-444.

HARLEY, J. L. and D. C. SMITH, 1956: Sugar absorption and surface carbohydrase activity of *Peltigera polydactyla* (*Neck.*) *Hoffm. Ann. Bot. N.S.* **20**, 513-543.

HARLEY, J. L. and J. M. WILSON, 1959: The absorption of potassium by beech mycorrhiza. *New. Phytol.* **58**, 281-298.

HEVESY, G., 1946: Interaction between the phosphorus atoms of the wheat seedling and the nutrient solution. *Ark. Bot.* **33**, 1-16.

HEVESY, G., K. LINDERSTRÖM-LANG and N. NIELSON, 1937: Phosphate exchange in yeast. *Nature, Lond.* **140**, 725.

HEVESY, G and N. NIELSON, 1941: Potassium interchange in yeast cells. *Acta physiol. scand.* **2**, 347-354.

HIGINBOTHAM, N., H. LATIMER and R. EPPLEY, 1953: Stimulation of rubidium absorption by auxins. *Science,* **118**, 243-245.

HIRAOKA, JUN-ICHI and H. TAKADA, 1957: Effect of ribonuclease on the methylene blue uptake and the sodium efflux by the yeast cell adapted to sodium chloride. *J. Inst. Polyt. Osaka, Ser. D,* **8**, 79-87.

HOAGLAND, D. R. and T. C. BROYER, 1942: Accumulation of salt and permeability in plant cells. *J. gen. Physiol.* **25**, 865-880.

HOAGLAND, D. R. and A. R. DAVIS, 1929: The intake and accumulation of electrolytes by plant cells. *Protoplasma,* **6**, 610-626.

HODGKIN, A. L., 1958: The Croonian Lecture. Ionic movements and electrical activity in giant nerve fibres. *Proc. roy. Soc. B,* **148**, 1-37.

HODGKIN, A. L. and R. D. KEYNES, 1955: The potassium permeability of a giant nerve fibre. *J. Physiol.* **128**, 61-88.

HOLM-JENSEN, I., A. KROGH and V. WARTIOVAARA, 1944: Some experiments on the exchange of potassium and sodium between single cells of Characeae and the bathing fluid. *Acta bot. fenn.* **36**, 1-22.

HOLTER, H., 1959: Pinocytosis. *Intern. Rev. Cytol.* **8**, 481-504.

HOLTER, H. and P. OTTOLENGHI, 1960: Observations on yeast protoplasts. *C. R. Lab. Carlsberg. Ser. Physiol.* **31**, 409-422.

van den HONERT, T. H., 1933: See Harley & McCready (1950).

van den HONERT, T. H. and J. J. M. HOOYMANS, 1955: On the absorption of nitrate by maize in water culture. *Acta Bot. Neerl.* **4**, 376-384.

HOPE, A. B., 1953: Salt uptake by root tissue cytoplasm: the relation between uptake and external concentration. *Aust J. Biol. Sci.* **6**, 396-409.

    1961: Ionic relations of cells of *Chara australis.* V. The action potential. *Aust. J. Biol. Sci.* **14**, 312-322.

HOPE, A. B. and P. G. STEVENS, 1952: Electrical potential differences in bean roots and their relation to salt uptake. *Aust. J. Sci. Res. B,* **5**, 335-343.

HOPE, A. B. and N. A. WALKER, 1961: Ionic relations of cells of *Chara australis* R. Br. IV. Membrane potential differences and resistances. *Aust. J. Biol. Sci.* **14**, 26-44.

HOTCHKISS, R. D., 1944: Gramicidin, tyrocidine and tyrothycin. *Advanc. Enzymol.* **4**, 153-199.

HURD, R. G., 1958: The effect of pH and bicarbonate ions on the uptake of salts by discs of red beet. *J. exp. Bot.* **9**, 159-174.

    1959: An effect of pH and bicarbonate on salt accumulation by discs of storage tissue. *J. exp. Bot.* **10**, 345-358.

HURWITZ, L., 1953: See Rothstein (1954).

HYLMO, B. 1953: Transpiration and ion absorption. *Physiol. Plant.* **6**, 333-405.

JACOBSON, L., R. J. HANNAPEL, D. P. MOORE and M. SCHAEDLE, 1961: Influence of calcium on selectivity of ion absorption processes. *Plant Physiol.* **36**, 58-61.

N*

JACOBSON, L., D. P. MOORE and R. J. HANNAPEL, 1960: Role of calcium in absorption of monovalent cations. *Plant Physiol.* **35**, 352-358.

JARNEFELT, J., 1961: Mechanism of sodium transport in cellular membranes. *Nature, Lond.* **190**, 694-697.

JENNINGS, D. H., 1956: D.Phil. Thesis, Oxford University. 120 p.

— 1958: Changes in the internal carbohydrates of beech mycorrhizas during treatment with azide. *New Phytol.* **57**, 254-255.

JENNINGS, D. H., D. C. HOOPER and A. ROTHSTEIN, 1958: The participation of phosphate in the formation of a 'carrier' for the transport of Mg^{++} and Mn^{++} ions into yeast cells. *J. gen. Physiol.* **41**, 1019-1026.

JENSEN, W. A. and A. D. McLAREN, 1960: Uptake of protein by plant cells. The possible occurrence of pinocytosis in plants. *Exp. Cell Res.* **19**, 414-417.

JUNI, E., M. D. KAMEN, J. M. REINER and S. SPIEGELMAN, 1948: Turnover and distribution of phosphate compounds in yeast metabolism. *Arch. Biochem.* **18**, 387-408.

KAHN, J. S. and J. B. HANSON, 1957: Effect of calcium on potassium accumulation in corn and soybean roots. *Plant Physiol.* **32**, 312-316.

KAMEN, M. D. and S. SPIEGELMAN, 1948: Studies on the phosphate metabolism of some unicellular organisms. *Cold Spring Harbor Symp.* **13**, 151-163.

KEILIN, D., 1959: The problem of anabiosis or latent life: history and current concepts. *Proc. roy. Soc. B*, **150**, 149-191.

KETCHUM, B. H., 1939: The absorption of phosphate and nitrate by illuminated cultures of *Nitzschia closterium*. *Amer. J. Bot.* **26**, 399-407.

KIHARA, H. and E. E. SNELL, 1952: Peptides and bacterial growth. II. L-alanine and growth of *Lactobacillus casei*. *J. biol. Chem.* **197**, 791-800.

KITCHENER, J. A., 1957: *Ion-Exchange resins*. London, Methuen, 109 pp.

KLEMPERER, H. G., 1957: The accumulation of iodide by *Fucus ceranoides*. *Biochem. J.* **67**, 381-390.

KUNITZ, M. and M. R. McDONALD, 1946: Crystalline hexokinase (heterophosphatase). Method of isolation and properties. *J. gen. Physiol.* **29**, 393-412.

LATIES, G. C., 1959a: Active transport of salt into plant tissues. *Annu. Rev. Pl. Physiol.* **10**, 87-112.

— 1959b: The nature of the respiratory rise in slices of chicory root. *Arch. Biochem.* **79**, 364-377.

— 1959c: The development and control of coexisting respiratory systems in slices of chicory root. *Arch. Biochem.* **79**, 378-391.

LEACH, F. R. and E. E. SNELL, 1959: Occurrence of independent uptake mechanisms for glycine and glycine peptides in *Lactobacillus casei*. *Biochem. biophys. Acta*, **34**, 292-293.

LE FEVRE, P. G., 1954: The evidence for active transport of monosaccharides across the red cell membrane. *Symp. Soc. exp. Biol.* **8**, 118-135.

— 1961: Sugar transport in the red blood cell: structure-activity relationships in substrates and antagonists. *Pharmacol. Revs.* **13**, 39-70.

LEGGETT, J. E. and E. EPSTEIN, 1956: Kinetics of sulfate absorption by barley roots. *Plant Physiol.* **31**, 222-226.

LINEWEAVER, H. and D. BURK, 1934: The determination of enzyme dissociation constants. *J. Amer. Chem. Soc.* **56**, 658-666.

LOEB, J., 1906: *The dynamics of living matter.* N.Y., The Colombia Univ. Press. 233 pp.

LOUGHMAN, B. C., 1957: The uptake and translocation of phosphate associated with respiration changes in potato slices. *Plant Physiol.* **37**, suppl. xxxvii.

— 1960: Uptake and utilization of phosphate associated with respiratory changes in potato tuber slices. *Plant Physiol.* **35**, 418-424.

LOUGHMAN, B. C. and R. S. RUSSELL, 1957: The absorption and utilization of phosphate by young barley plants. IV. The initial stages of phosphate metabolism in roots. *J. exp. Bot.* **8**, 280-293.

LUNDEGÅRDH, H., 1940: Investigations into the absorption and accumulation of inorganic ions. *Lantbr. Högsk. Ann.* **8**, 233-404.

— 1951: Spectroscopic evidence of the participation of the cytochrome —cytochrome oxidase system in the active transport of salts. *Ark. Kemi.*, **3**, 69-79.

— 1954: Anion respiration: the experimental basis of a theory of absorption, transport and exudation of electrolytes by living cells and tissues. *Symp. Soc. exp. Biol.* **8**, 262-296.

— 1955: Mechanisms of absorption, transport, accumulation and secretion of ions. *Annu. Rev. Pl. Physiol.* **6**, 1-24.

— 1959: Investigations on the mechanism of absorption and accumulation of salts IV. Synergistic and antagonistic effects of anions. *Physiol. Plant.* **12**, 336-341.

LUNDEGÅRDH, H. and H. BURSTRÖM, 1933a: Atmung und Ionenaufnahme. *Planta*, **18**, 683-699.

— 1933: Untersuchungen über die Salzaufnahme der Pflanzen. III. Quantitative Beziehungen zwischen Atmung und Anionenaufnahme. *Biochem. Z.* **261**, 235-251.

— 1935: Untersuchungen über die Atmungsvorgänge in Pflanzenwurzeln. *Biochem. Z.* **277**, 223-249.

MACDONALD, I. R. and P. C. DE KOCK, 1958: Temperature control and metabolic drifts in ageing disks of storage tissue. *Ann. Bot. N.S.* **22**, 429-448.

MACMILLAN, A., 1956a: The entry of ammonia into fungal cells. *J. exp. Bot.* **7**, 113-126.

— 1956b: The entry of nitrates into fungal cells. *Physiol. Plant.* **9**, 470-481.

MACROBBIE, E. A. C. and J. DAINTY, 1958: Ion transport in *Nitellopsis obtusa. J. gen. Physiol.* **42**, 335-353.

MALEY, F. and H. A. LARDY, 1955: Synthesis of N-substituted glucosamines and their effect on hexokinase. *J. biol. Chem.* **214**, 765-774.

MANTON, I., 1961: Plant Cell Structure. *Contemporary Botanical Thought* (ed. A. M. McLeod and L. S. Cobley). Edinburgh, Oliver & Boyd. 171-97.

MARTIN, R. P. and R. S. RUSSELL, 1950: Studies with radioactive tracers in plant nutrition. II. The estimation of radioactive tracers. *J. exp. Bot.* **1**, 141-158.

MERCER, F. V., A. J. HODGE, A. B. HOPE and J. D. McLEAN, 1955: The structure and swelling properties of *Nitella* chloroplasts. *Austr. J. Biol. Sci.* **8**, 1-18.

✓MIDDLETON, L. J. and R. S. RUSSELL, 1958: The interaction of cations in absorption by plant tissues. *J. exp. Bot.* **9**, 115-127.

MITCHELL, P., 1953: Transport of phosphate across the surface of *Micrococcus pyogenes*: nature of the cell 'inorganic phosphate'. *J. gen. Microbiol.* **9**, 273-287.

1954: Transport of phosphate across the osmostic barrier of *Micrococcus pyogenes*: specificity and kinetics. *J. gen. Microbiol.* **11**, 73-82.

1959: Structure and function in microorganisms. *Symp. Biochem. Soc.* **16**, 73-93.

1961: Coupling of phosphorylation to electron and hydrogen transfer by a chemi-osmotic type of mechanism. *Nature, Lond.* **191**, 144-148.

MITCHELL, P. and J. MOYLE, 1956: Osmotic function and structure in bacteria. *Symp. Soc. gen. Microbiol.* **6**, 150-180.

MOORE, D. P., R. OVERSTREET and L. JACOBSON, 1961: Uptake of magnesium and its interaction with calcium in excised barley roots. *Plant Physiol.* **36**, 290-295.

MORTON, A. G., 1956: A study of nitrate reduction in mold fungi. *J. exp. Bot.* **7**, 97-112.

MORTON, A. G. and A. MACMILLAN, 1954: Assimilation of nitrogen from ammonium salts and nitrate by fungi. *J. exp. Bot.* **5**, 232-252.

MULLINS, L. J., 1942: The permeability of yeast cells to radiophosphate. *Biol. Bull., Wood's Hole*, **83**, 326-333.

1959: An analysis of conductance changes in squid axon. *J. gen. Physiol.* **42**, 1013-1035.

MYRBÄCK, K. and E. WILLSTAEDT, 1955: Studies on yeast invertase (saccharase): localisation of the enzyme in the cell and its liberation. *Ark. Kemi.* **8**, 367-374.

NAJJAR, V. and E. F. GALE, 1950: The assimilation of amino-acids by bacteria. 9. The passage of lysine across the cell wall of *Streptococcus faecalis. Biochem. J.* **46**, 91-95.

NICKERSON, W. J. and G. FALCONE, 1956: Enzymic reduction of disulphide bonds in cell wall protein of baker's yeast. *Science*, **124**, 318-319.

O'KANE, D. J. and W. W. UMBREIT, 1942: Transformations of phosphorus during glucose fermentation by living cells of *Streptococcus faecalis. J. biol. Chem.* **142**, 25-30.

OSTERHOUT, W. J. V., 1906: On the importance of physiologically balanced solutions. I. Marine plants. *Bot. Gaz.* **42**, 127-134.

1931: Physiological studies of single plant cells. *Biol. Rev.* **6**, 369-411.

OSTERHOUT, W. J. V. and S. E. HILL, 1935: Nature of the action current in *Nitella*. III. Some additional features. *J. gen. Physiol.* **18**, 499-514.

PASSOW, H. and A. ROTHSTEIN, 1960: The binding of mercury by the yeast cell in relation to changes in permeability. *J. gen. Physiol.* **43**, 621-633.

Passow, H. A. Rothstein and B. Loewenstein, 1959: An all-or-none response in the release of potassium by yeast cells treated with methylene blue and other basic redox dyes. *J. gen. Physiol.* **43**, 97-107.

Pennell, G. A. and P. E. Weatherley, 1958: On the mechanism of sugar uptake by floating leaf discs. *New Phytol.* **57**, 326-339.

Pickles, V. R. and J. F. Sutcliffe, 1955: The effects of 5-hydroxytryptamine, indole-3-acetic acid and some other substances on pigment effusion, Na uptake and K efflux by slices of red beetroot *in vitro*. *Biochim. biophys. Acta*, **17**, 244-251.

Post, R. L., C. R. Merritt, C. R. Kinsolving and C. D. Albright, 1960: Membrane adenosine tryphosphatase as a participant in the active transport of sodium and potassium in the human erythrocyte. *J. Biol. Chem.* **235**, 1796-1802.

Reinhold, L., 1958: Release of ammonia by plant tissues treated with indole-3-acetic acid. *Nature, Lond.* **182**, 1022-1023.

Reinhold, L. and R. G. Powell, 1958: The stimulatory effect of indole-3-acetic acid on the uptake of amino-acids by tissues of *Helianthus annuus*. *J. exp. Bot.* **9**, 82-96.

Roberts, R. B. and I. Z. Roberts, 1950: Potassium metabolism in *Escherichia coli*. III. Interrelationships of potassium and phosphorus metabolism. *J. cell. comp. Physiol.* **36**, 15-39.

Roberts, R. B., I. Z. Roberts and D. B. Cowie, 1949: Potassium metabolism in *Escherichia coli*. II. Metabolism in the presence of carbohydrates and their metabolic derivatives. *J. cell. comp. Physiol.* **34**, 259-291.

Robertson, J. J. and H. O. Halvorson, 1957: The components of maltozymase in yeast and their behaviour during deadaptation. *J. Bact.* **73**, 186-198.

Robertson, R. N., 1940: Salt accumulation and plant respiration. *Nature, Lond.* **145**, 937-938.

  1941: Studies in the metabolism of plant cells. I. Accumulation of chlorides by plant cells and its relation to respiration. *Austr. J. exp. Biol. & med. Sci.* **19**, 265-278.

  1956: The mechanism of absorption. *Encyclopedia of Plant Physiology* (Ed. W. Ruhland). Berlin, Springer-Verlag. **2**, 449-467.

Robertson, R. N. and J. S. Turner, 1945: Studies in the metabolism of plant cells. IV. The effects of cyanide on the accumulation of KCl and on respiration; the nature of salt respiration. *Austr. J. exp. Biol. & med. Sci.* **23**, 63-73.

Robertson, R. N., J. S. Turner and M. J. Wilkins, 1947: Studies in the metabolism of plant cells. V. Salt respiration and accumulation in red beet tissues. *Austr. J. exp. Biol. med. Sci.* **25**, 1-8.

Robertson, R. N., M. J. Wilkins, A. B. Hope and L. Nestel, 1955: Studies in the metabolism of plant cells. X. Respiratory activity and ionic relations of plant mitochondria. *Austr. J. Biol. Sci.* **8**, 164-185.

Robertson, R. N., M. J. Wilkins and D. C. Weeks, 1951: Studies in the metabolism of plant cells. IX. The effects of 2-4: dinitrophenol on salt accumulation and salt respiration. *Austr. J. Sci. Res. B*, **4**, 248-264.

ROSENBERG, TH., 1954: The concept and definition of active transport. *Symp. Soc. exp. Biol.* **8**, 27-41.

ROSENBERG, TH. and W. WILBRANDT, 1952: Enzymatic processes in cell membrane penetration. *Intern. Rev. Cytol.* **1**, 65-92.

ROTHSTEIN, A., 1954: Enzyme systems of the cell surface involved in the uptake of sugars by yeast. *Symp. Soc. exp. Biol.* **8**, 165-201.

    1956: Compartmentalization of the cell surface of yeast in relation to metabolic activities. *Disc. Faraday Soc.* No. **21**, 229-238.

ROTHSTEIN, A. and M. BRUCE, 1958a: The potassium efflux and influx in yeast at different potassium concentrations. *J. cell. comp. Physiol.* **51**, 145-160.

    1958b: The efflux of potassium from yeast cells into a potassium-free medium. *J. cell. comp. Physiol.* **51**, 439-455.

ROTHSTEIN, A. and C. DEMIS, 1953: The relationship of the cell surface to metabolism. The stimulation of fermentation by extra-cellular potassium. *Arch. Biochem.* **44**, 18-29.

ROTHSTEIN, A. and L. H. ENNS, 1946: The relationship of potassium to carbohydrate metabolism in baker's yeast. *J. cell. comp. Physiol.* **28**, 231-252.

ROTHSTEIN, A., A. FRENKEL and C. LARRABEE, 1948: The relationship of the cell surface to metabolism. III. Certain characteristics of the uranium complex with cell surface groups of yeast. *J. cell. comp. Physiol.* **32**, 261-274.

ROTHSTEIN, A. and A. D. HAYES, 1956: The relationship of the cell surface to metabolism. XIII. The cation-binding properties of the yeast cell surface. *Arch. Biochem.* **63**, 87-99.

ROTHSTEIN, A., A. D. HAYES, D. H. JENNINGS and D. C. HOOPER, 1958: The active transport of Mg^{++} and Mn^{++} into the yeast cell. *J. gen. Physiol.* **41**, 585-594.

ROTHSTEIN, A., D. H. JENNINGS, C. DEMIS and M. BRUCE, 1959: The relationship of fermentation to cell structure in yeast. *Biochem. J.* **71**, 99-106.

ROTHSTEIN, A. and R. MEIER, 1948: The relationship of the cell surface to metabolism. I. Phosphatases in the cell surface of living yeast cells. *J. cell. comp. Physiol.* **32**, 77-95.

ROTHSTEIN, A. and R. MEIER, 1951: The relationship of the cell surface to metabolism. VI. The chemical nature of uranium-complexing groups of the cell surface. *J. cell. comp. Physiol.* **38**, 245-270.

ROTHSTEIN, A., R. MEIER and L. HURWITZ, 1951: The relationship of the cell surface to metabolism. V. The role of uranium-complexing loci of yeast in metabolism. *J. cell. comp. Physiol.* **37**, 57-82.

ROWLANDS, D. A., E. F. GALE, J. P. FOLKES and D. H. MARRIAN, 1957: The assimilation of amino acids by bacteria. 23. Accumulation of free glutamic acid within *Staphlococcus aureus* incubated with derivatives of glutamic acid. *Biochem. J.* **65**, 519-526.

RUSSELL, R. S. and R. P. MARTIN, 1953: A study of the absorption and utilisation of phosphate by young barley plants. 1. The effect of external concentration on the distribution of absorbed phosphate between shoots and roots. *J. exp. Bot.* **4**, 108-127.

RUSTAD, R. C., 1961: Pinocytosis. *Sci. Amer.* **204**, 120-133.

SAMSON, F. E., A. M. KATZ and D. L. HARRIS, 1955: Effects of acetate and other short-chain acids on yeast metabolism. *Arch. Biochem.* **54**, 406-423.

SCHARFF, T. G. and J. L. BECK, 1959: Effects of surface-active agents on carbohydrate metabolism in yeast. *Proc. Soc. exp. Biol., N.Y.* **100**, 307-311.

SCHARFF, T. G. and W. C. MAUPIN, 1960: Correlation of the metabolic effects of benzalkonium chloride with its membrane effects in yeast. *Biochem. Pharmacol.* **5**, 79-86.

SCHATZMANN, H. J., 1953: Herzglykoside als Hemmstoffe für der aktiven Kalcium- und Natrium transport durch die Erythrocytenmembran. *Helv. physiol. acta*, **11**, 346-354.

SCOTT, G. T. and H. R. HAYWARD, 1953a: Metabolic factors influencing the sodium and potassium distribution in *Ulva lactuca*. *J. gen. Physiol.* **36**, 659-671.

    1953b: Influence of temperature and illumination on the exchange of potassium ion in *Ulva lactuca*. *Biochim. biophys. Acta*, **12**, 401-404.

    1954: Evidence for the presence of separate mechanisms regulating K^+ and Na^+ distribution in *Ulva lactuca*. *J. gen. Physiol.* **37**, 601-620.

    1955: Sodium & potassium regulation in *Ulva lactuca* and *Valonia macrophysa*. *Electrolytes in Biological Systems* (Ed. A. M. Shanes). Washington, Amer. Physiol. Soc. 35-64.

SCOTT, G. T., R. DE VOE, H. R. HAYWARD and G. CRAVEN, 1957: Exchange of sodium ions in *Ulva lactuca*. *Science*, **125**, 160.

SCOTT, R. and L-E. ERICSON, 1955: Some aspects of cobalt metabolism by *Rhodemenia palmata* with particular reference to vitamin B_{12} content. *J. exp. Bot.* **6**, 348-361.

SHAW, T. I., 1955: Potassium movements in washed erythrocytes. *J. Physiol.* **129**, 464-475.

    1959: The mechanism of iodide accumulation by the brown seaweed *Laminaria digitata*. 1. The uptake of [131]I. *Proc. roy. Soc. B*, **150**, 356-371.

SHAW, W. N. and W. C. STADIE, 1959: Two identical Embden-Meyerhof enzyme systems in normal rat diaphragms differing in cytological location and response to insulin. *J. biol. Chem.* **234**, 2491-2496.

SHRIFT, A. 1954: Sulphur-selenium antagonism. 1. Antimetabolite action of selenate on the growth of *Chlorella vulgaris*. *Amer. J. Bot.* **41**, 223-230.

SIDERIS, C. P., B. H. KRAUSS and H. Y. YOUNG, 1937: Assimilation of ammonium and nitrate nitrogen from solution cultures by the roots of *Pandanus veichii* Hort. and distribution of various nitrogen fractions and sugars in stele and cortex. *Plant Physiol.* **12**, 899-928.

SIEKEVITZ, P., 1959: On the meaning of intracellular structure for metabolic regulation. *The Regulation of Cell Metabolism*, CIBA Foundation Symp. (Ed. G. E. W. Wolstenholme and C. M. O'Connor). London, Churchill, 17-45.

SIMON, E. W. and H. BEEVERS, 1952: The effect of pH on the biological activity of weak acids and bases. 1. The most usual relationship between pH and activity. *New Phytol.* **51**, 163-190.

SKOU, J. C., 1957: The influence of some cations on an adenosine triphosphatase from peripheral nerves. *Biochim. biophys. Acta*, **23**, 394-401.

1960: Further investigations on a Mg++ + Na+ -activated adenosine triphosphatase possibly related to the active, linked transport of Na+ and K+ across the nerve membrane. *Biochim, biophys. Acta*, **42**, 6-23.

STEIN, W. D., 1961a: Dimer formation and the transfer of glycol across the erythrocyte membrane. *Nature, Lond.* **191**, 352-355.

1961b: Dimer formation and glucose transfer across the membrane of the red blood cell. *Nature, Lond.* **191**, 1277-1280.

STEIN, W. D. and J. F. DANIELLI, 1956: Structure and functions in red cell permeability. *Disc. Faraday Soc.* No. **21**, 238-251.

STENLID, G., 1959: On the effect of some sugars and of 2-4 : dinitrophenol upon the absorption of phosphate ions by excised roots. *Physiol. Plant.* **12**, 199-217.

STEWARD, F. C., 1930: The absorption and accumulation of solutes by living plant cells. 1. Experimental conditions which determine salt absorption by storage tissue. *Protoplasma*, **11**, 521-557.

STEWARD, F. C. and J. C. MARTIN, 1937: The distribution and physiology of *Valonia* at the Dry Tortugas with special reference to the problem of salt accumulation. *Publ. Carneg. Instn.* **475**, 87-170.

STEWARD, F. C. and F. K. MILLAR, 1954: Salt accumulation in plants. A reconsideration of the role of growth and metabolism. *Symp. Soc. exp. Biol.* **8**, 367-406.

STEWARD, F. C. and J. F. SUTCLIFFE, 1959: Plants in relation to inorganic salts. *Plant Physiology* (Ed. F. C. Steward). N.Y., Academic Press, **2**, 235-478.

STILES, W. and A. D. SKELDING, 1940: The salt relations of plant tissues. II. The absorption of manganese chloride by storage tissue. *Ann. Bot. N.S.* **4**, 637-700.

STREET, H. E., A. E. KENYON and G. M. WATSON, 1946: The assimilation of ammonium and nitrate nitrogen by detached potato sprouts. *Ann. appl. Biol.* **33**, 369-381.

STREET, H. E. and J. S. LOWE, 1950: On the carbohydrate nutrition of tomato roots. II. The mechanism of sucrose absorption by excised roots. *Ann. Bot. N.S.* **14**, 307-329.

SUTCLIFFE, J. F., 1952: The influence of internal ion concentration on potassium accumulation and salt respiration of red beet root tissue. *J. exp. Bot.* **3**, 59-76.

1954: The exchangeability of potassium and bromide ions in cells of red beet root tissue. *J. exp. Bot.* **5**, 313-327.

1957: The selective uptake of alkali cations by red beet root tissue. *J. exp. Bot.* **8**, 36-49.

SUTCLIFFE, J. F. and E. R. COUNTER, 1959: Absorption of alkali cations by plant tissue cultures. *Nature, Lond.* **183**, 1513-1514.

TANADA, T., 1956: Effect of sulfydryl inhibitors on rubidium absorption by excised mung bean roots. *Plant. Physiol.* **31**, 403-406.

TAYLOR, E. S., 1947: The assimilation of amino acids by bacteria. 3. Concentration of free amino acids in the internal environment of various bacteria and yeasts. *J. gen. Microbiol.* **1**, 86-90.

TAYLOR, F. J., 1960a: The absorption of glucose by *Scenedesmus quadricauda.* I. Some kinetic aspects. *Proc. roy. Soc. B,* **151**, 400-418.

1960b: The absorption of glucose by *Scendesmus quadricauda.* II. The nature of the absorption process. *Proc. roy. Soc. B,* **151**, 483-496.

TEORELL, T., 1949: Membrane electrophoresis in relation to bio-electrical polarisation effects. *Arch. Sci. physiol.* **3**, 205-219.

USSING, H. H., 1947: Interpretation of the exchange of radio-sodium in isolated muscle. *Nature, Lond.* **160**, 262-263.

1949: The distinction by means of tracers between active transport and diffusion. The transfer of iodide across the isolated frog skin. *Acta physiol. scand.* **19**, 43-55.

1960: The alkali metal ions in biology. I. The alkali metal ions in isolated systems and tissues. *Handbuch der experimentellan pharmakologie* (Ed. O. Eichler and A. Farah). Berlin, Springer-Verlag. **13**, 1-195.

UTTER, M. F., D. B. KEECH and P. M. NOSSAL, 1958: Oxidative phosphorylation by subcellular particles from yeast. *Biochem. J.* **68**, 431-440.

VIETS, F. G., 1944: Calcium and other polyvalent cations as accelerators of ion accumulation by excised barley roots. *Plant Physiol.* **19**, 466-480.

WALKER, N. A., 1955: Microelectrode experiments on *Nitella. Aust. J. Biol. Sci.* **8**, 476-489.

1957: Ion permeability of the plasmalemma of the plant cell. *Nature, Lond.* **180**, 94-95.

1958: Ion permeability of the plasmalemma of the plant cell. *Nature, Lond.* **181**, 1288-1289.

WEATHERLEY, P. E., 1953: On the uptake and hydrolysis of sucrose by leaf tissues. *New Phytol.* **52**, 76-79.

1954: Preliminary investigations into the uptake of sugars by floating leaf disks. *New Phytol.* **53**, 204-216.

WEISSMAN, G. S., 1950: Growth and nitrogen absorption of wheat seedlings as influenced by the ammonium: nitrate ratio and the hydrogen-ion concentration. *Amer. J. Bot.* **37**, 725-738.

WEISSMAN, G. S. and S. F. TRELEASE, 1955: Influence of sulfur on the toxicity of selenium to *Aspergillus. Amer. J. Bot.* **42**, 489-495.

WHITTAM, R., 1961: Active cation transport as a pace-maker of respiration. *Nature, Lond.* **191**, 603-604.

WILBRANDT, W., 1954: Secretion and transport of non-electrolytes. *Symp. Soc. exp. Biol.* **8**, 136-162.

WIAME, J. M., 1949: The occurrence and physiological behaviour of two meta-phosphate fractions in yeast. *J. biol. Chem.* **178**, 919-929.

WILLIAMS, D. E. and N. T. COLEMAN, 1950: Cation exchange properties of plant root surfaces. *Plant and Soil,* **2**, 243-256.

INDEX